LYALL WATSON

The author was born in Africa and educated there and in Britain, taking his doctorate in animal behaviour under the supervision of Desmond Morris at London Zoo.

He has been involved in anthropology in Indonesia and Brazil, archaeology in Jordan and Peru, palaeontology in South and East Africa, and marine biology in the Indian Ocean – representing Seychelles on the International Whaling Commission.

For the past fifteen years, he has been pursuing the paranormal, travelling constantly from his base in the far west of Ireland, pausing only to publish his bestsellers SUPERNATURE, THE BIOLOGY OF DEATH (formerly entitled THE ROMEO ERROR), GIFTS OF UNKNOWN THINGS, LIFETIDE and HEAVEN'S BREATH.

Lyall Watson's recent books include WHALES OF THE WORLD, DREAMS OF DRAGONS (published in hardback as EARTHWORKS) and SUPER-NATURE II (published in hardback as BEYOND SUPERNATURE). He is working on THE SECRET LIFE OF MACHINES and a biography of Raymond Dart, the discoverer of the first African apeman.

Praise for LYALL WATSON

HEAVEN'S BREATH
'A comprehensive and fascinating study'
Bernard Levin's Book Of The Year,
The Observer, 1984

LIGHTNING BIRD
'A remarkable, brilliant book'
Daily Mail

DREAMS OF DRAGONS
'An outstanding view of the world from an outstanding
author . . . thought-provoking and stimulating . . . a
must for anyone who wants to sample the occasional
original thought'
Guernsey Evening Press and Star

SUPERNATURE II
'Mr Watson is not afraid to think the unthinkable:
for instance that miracles might be actually quite
common, but simply unnoticed most of the time.
His open-mindedness is refreshing'
Daily Telegraph

Lyall Watson

OMNIVORE
The Role of Food in
Human Evolution

First published in Great Britain in 1971 by Souvenir Press Ltd.

Corgi edition, 1973
Sceptre edition 1988

Sceptre is an imprint of Hodder and Stoughton Paperbacks, a division of Hodder and Stoughton Ltd.

British Library C.I.P.

Watson, Lyall
  Omnivore: the role of food in human evolution.
  1. Man. Food habits.
  Compared with animal feeding behaviour.
  2. Animals. Feeding behaviour. Compared with human food habits.
  I. Title
  394.1

ISBN 0-340-42856-2

Printed and bound in Great Britain for Hodder and Stoughton Paperbacks, a division of Hodder and Stoughton Ltd., Mill Road, Dunton Green, Sevenoaks, Kent TN13 2YA (Editorial Office: 47 Bedford Square, London WC1B 3DP) by Richard Clay Ltd., Bungay, Suffolk. Photoset by Rowland Phototypesetting Ltd., Bury St Edmunds, Suffolk.

CONTENTS

	Introduction	9
	Preface	11
1	Food	13
2	Feeders	27
3	Finding Food	43
4	Keeping Food	63
5	Preparing Food	79
6	Eating	95
7	Drinking	111
8	Food and Sex	121
9	Food for Thought	137
	Postscript	155

INTRODUCTION

This was my first book. It was drafted in the early sixties while I was still working for my doctorate under the supervision of Desmond Morris at London Zoo.

Those were magic years. I was just twenty-two, fresh from Africa, London was beginning to swing and with Desmond there, constantly flexing his lively imagination, I was enthralled.

The Naked Ape was in the making and each day Desmond came to work – in truth it was more like wonderfully creative play – filled with enthusiasm for some outrageous new idea. We would spend every free moment that day exploring all the implications and then the following morning he would arrive, wedded now to some totally contradictory hypothesis, convinced (as he had been the day before) that *this* was the key that would lead to a breakthrough in our understanding of both human and animal behaviour.

It was impossible, in such a stimulating environment, not to begin making patterns of my own. And, as I had chosen to study the feeding behaviour of a wide variety of species in the Zoo, this book was the result.

It was not published for another ten years. But reading it now, fifteen years later still, I find myself filled once again with the exhilaration of those heady days. I hope that a little of that excitement comes through to you too.

LYALL WATSON
Ballydehob, Eire; 1987

PREFACE

Humans have come a long way. We can trace our physical progress through several million years of fossil records. But knowledge of our mental development is much less complete. Behaviour has no hard parts that survive in fossil form, but old habits do linger on as an after-image on patterns we still use today. Of all these patterns, those connected with feeding seem to contain the greatest number of relics.

For this reason I have chosen to look at evolution only as seen through man's mouth.

I have deliberately isolated feeding from all other aspects of behaviour because I believe it to be the most fundamental. This is obviously an artificial approach to the study of anything so complex as man, but I believe that it has some merit. In captivity, even the wildest animal continues to eat – and, given the proper opportunities, it does so in exactly the same way as its less restricted relatives. In the human zoo, man eats some strange things, but I hope to show that his choice of food and feeding site and the way in which he deals with his meal, are a true reflection of his oral origins.

This is just a peep through the dining-room window, but it is one that can be very revealing.

LYALL WATSON
The Great Rift Valley, 1971

ONE

FOOD

More of our waking hours are spent in feeding than in any other single activity. Our days are divided into convenient portions, each separated from the other by a break for taking in some kind of food. And, often as not, the portions between the breaks are filled with the effects of the last meal or the thoughts of the next.

We are seldom free from the pressures put upon us by our stomachs. It has always been this way. The only reason that we do not spend even more time finding, preparing, and preserving food is that our society is so arranged that a few specialise in these functions, leaving the rest of us free to carry on with more creative activities. Like writing about food.

The average human stomach has a ton of food in it each year, so it is hardly surprising that food should interest us as much as it does. But it *is* surprising that this interest should be coupled with so little understanding. Most of us are brain-washed at an early age into various comfortable notions about food and feeding. We learn, for instance, that nice people do not eat dogs. An idea reinforced by a cautionary tale about an American who was recently found guilty of cruelty to animals and given the maximum sentence allowed by the state of Illinois, just because he cooked a dead stray dog. He never got the chance to eat it.

Our ideas about animal feeding behaviour are even more peculiar. We learn that rabbits eat lettuce and donkeys eat carrots and mice eat cheese. And that is that – all very nice and tidy. These pigeonhole ideas are so widespread and persistent that in a zoo one becomes used to hearing exclamations of surprise that the food provided should be so varied. Even zoologists fall into the trap of classifying mammals as carnivores or herbivores and are continually surprised to discover that foxes consume large quantities of wild fruits and that small antelope will kill and eat birds.

Pigeonholes are for pigeons. It is hopeless trying to squeeze pangolins and people into them. Where feeding behaviour is concerned, it is impossible. People, in particular, are apt to eat almost anything. In many parts of the world dogs are raised only for food. Roast puppies are served as a delicacy on special occasions. It is possible that the dog was first domesticated as a dinner rather than a houseguest. The Egyptians, Greeks and Aztecs all ate dog. The Romans said it tasted rather like hare. We in the West have a taboo on it at the moment which is strong enough in some places to cause public prosecutions. But one of the most popular foods in that very same community goes under the name hot dog. Food fashions change all the time. In the pages that follow, I will trace the course of some of these changes and show how they have played a vital part in the development of man. The story begins with some close relatives of ours – the mammals.

One thing that most mammals have in common, besides fur and warm blood and suckled young, is adaptability. They have been extraordinarily successful because of their free interpretation of the principle of survival of the fittest. This has been made possible by the development of a large and active brain. It is only natural that they should apply their burgeoning intelligence to the biggest single problem in their lives – the daily chore of finding enough to eat. They have made it into a sort of game in which the losers lose their lives. While specialising in one particular field of feeding in order to gain an advantage over their competitors, most species have remained free to adapt their diet to changing circumstances.

Change is taking place all the time, and because eating happens every day, it is the best possible barometer of change.

We just have to look at an animal's feeding behaviour, and this one aspect of its whole complicated repertoire will tell us most of what we need to know about its individual welfare and about the status of its species. The same applies to man, the most adaptable and successful mammal. But, to make this kind of assessment successfully, we need to get rid of all misconceptions about food and feeding. We need to separate the myth from the mouth.

Certainly mice eat cheese; but they have also been known to eat wheat, meat, fruit, jute, eggs, onions, nuts, sugar, salt, ivory, tobacco, paper, polythene bags and the fingers of ladies' gloves. The fact that they eat cheese tells us nothing. I have seen both camels and carp eating cheese. But the fact that mice also eat all those *other* things is far more interesting. It tells us that mice are opportunistic and exploratory – and probably highly successful. They are.

A great deal can be inferred from a knowledge only of the type of food an animal eats. If information about a species is limited, the one thing a zoologist would most like to know – and that will tell him more than any other single fact – is: what does it eat? One could almost say, as an eighteenth-century gastronomist once did, 'Tell me what you eat and I will tell you what you are.' He was thinking of the class distinctions which were revealed at that time by a man's choice of food, but the principle can also be applied to animal food preferences. For instance, from the information that you ate nothing but ants, I could infer that you probably had a long sticky tongue and needed only tiny teeth. That you had a long thin face to house the long thin tongue and to enable you to get closer to your work. That your sense of smell was good and that your eyes, being largely unnecessary, were rather weak. That you were of a retiring nature and probably nocturnal because it is safer at night and anytime is a good time for eating ants. That your body would be covered with either long hair or armour to protect you from your food. That your front legs were nicely adapted for digging holes in the ground and that you could, if provoked, use these as weapons of defence.

I could also predict that, if all this is true, your days are numbered. There was a time when you ate other things as well as ants, but you never will again. You have gambled everything on ants. So far, the gamble has paid off because the ants are still around and you have specialised to such an extent that nobody else eats ants as well as you do. But what if something should happen to the ants? With all your evolutionary eggs in one specialised basket, you would be unable to adapt and would quickly follow the ant into antiquity.

If you were in fact a mammalian anteater, then I would be perfectly correct. This is exactly how anteaters have evolved, and these are precisely the risks involved. But there is a limit to the kind of inference that can be drawn from a knowledge only of the food. I could have been completely wrong. There are some birds that eat ants – and they are nothing like this. To play this zoological guessing game well, one needs to have more information. But it is still, at best, only an academic parlour game. The real one is played for far higher stakes in a much larger arena.

Eating is a global game – everyone has to play. The players are divided up into teams or species. Many teams take the field at the same time, but direct competition takes place only between teams in the same league who are after the same food prizes. It is a knockout competition. The winners of each bout go on to play and eat again. The losers lose everything – even their lives. The rules of the game are simple. Teams are permitted to introduce any innovation that might give them a selective advantage over their rivals. They usually do this by getting one of their players to try out the new move or the new food first. If it works, the whole team will use it. But if it fails, only the individual player is penalised by being sent off the field. He is immediately replaced by a member of the opposing team. Cautious teams which refrain from making plays can profit from their opponent's mistakes in this way, but they can equally well lose by default and die of starvation. A season of competition may last a very long time, so in the end only the fittest teams survive to eat at the top of the league table. There is no end to the game and no question of retirement. Champions enjoy the best foods and the title of top species, but they have to defend their table and their title all the time.

The game has been going on now for two billion years. During this time there have been many top teams, each holding the title for a while and then disappearing from the competition altogether. Some species remained on top for 100,000,000 years but failed even in all this time to open up a safe gap between themselves and their nearest rivals. They were eventually replaced. But in the current season a vital young team has arrived on the Pleistocene and introduced a whole new style of play. They have taken chances that could have ended in disaster. But they have been lucky and gone on instead to a series of resounding victories that gave them a more commanding lead than any other team has ever had. This incredibly successful species is so far out in front that it has been able, for the first time ever, to keep some of its players on the sidelines. No previous team could afford to carry non-playing passengers, but the new league leaders have changed all that. They have given the game its first spectators.

I am one of these. I believe that of all the games that people play, this one is the most revealing. We can learn a great deal just by turning the spotlight on man's mouth and watching him eat. Feeding behaviour is so fundamental and so widespread and so easy to see. Everybody does it – and usually right out in the open. There are a few secret eaters, but there is no need for the student of feeding to have to rely, like the student of sex, on what other people tell him. Eating is a spectator sport. It takes place in a field ripe for scientific investigation. One that opens up a new approach to human behaviour. The gut method provides insights which cannot be obtained in any other way. And it provides a perfect opportunity for using the techniques of the comparative ethologist. All animals play the same game by the same rules and are subject to the same kind of analysis.

Anthropologists have a hard time finding even one way in which man differs absolutely from the other animals. Every time they think of one, along comes a zoologist with proof that some animal or other has been doing it for years. They used to say that man was 'the tool-using animal', but even Egyptian vultures break ostrich eggs by throwing stones at them. 'Tool-making animal' has been abandoned since it was discovered that chimps feed on termites with straws specially prepared for the purpose. The last stronghold of the Man-is-Unique school of thought was in the apparently unassailable catch-phrase 'man is the only animal capable of abstract thought'. But even this has been demolished by the zoologist's newest and most powerful weapon – the dolphin. Research has shown that dolphins have a special method for dealing with sharks and that it is not innate but has to be learned. Baby dolphins reared in isolation never learn it. But dolphins reared by their mothers, even in the absence of sharks, know exactly what to do the very first time they meet one on their own. Mother dolphins tell their offspring that there is such a thing as a shark, that it looks like this, and that as soon as you see it you should go and butt it hard, here, just behind the pectoral fin. So dolphins have an ability to think in the abstract which almost amounts to a folklore. And man loses another distinction.

It becomes clear that the differences between human and other animal behaviour are more quantitative than qualitative. It is often just a matter of degree, but even though they are on the same scale, man and his nearest rival are still a long distance apart. A great gulf separates human language from even the most sophisticated animal system of communication. Human technology is way ahead of animal know-how. Man's sexual and aggressive behaviour is considerably more complex than that of any animal. There are barber fish and mammals with comb teeth, but nowhere is there anything like the elaborate industry that has grown up around human comfort behaviour. In all these respects, human and non-human animals are poles apart. But there is one field of behaviour in which the gulf is not so great. The response to food. Only in feeding does the gap narrow to a point where differences sometimes disappear altogether and valid comparisons can be made.

Man hunts with a weapon; baboons kill snakes with stones. Man domesticates food animals; ants keep herds of aphids and milk them for sugar water. Man cultivates food plants; termites

grow fungi in carefully tended gardens. Man stores food surpluses; hamsters accumulate enormous hoards. Man preserves
his food before storing it; squirrels lay mushrooms out to dry
in the sun before burying them. Man eats with an implement;
chimps lick ants off a straw that they push down suitable holes.
Man prepares food by chemical means; orangs bury certain
leaves until they ferment and become edible. There are many
parallels and few points of divergence. One of the few differences is that man cooks his food, but even here there are
similarities. Cooking is in effect a sort of external, partial
predigestion. Hunting dogs do that. Members of the pack,
returning from a successful hunt, regurgitate partly digested
food for their young. This is a kind of cooking, even if it happens
to be done in someone else's stomach.

The resemblance between human and animal feeding behaviour is too close to ignore. It is one of the most powerful
research tools at our disposal. With it we can pick out any
aspect of human feeding and fit it into a complete spectrum of
behaviour patterns that runs all the way from the most simple
to the most complex. In many instances the human pattern will
fall into place at the upper end of the scale, and by looking back
down the evolutionary line, we can see where it came from.
But in several cases it belongs somewhere in the middle of the
series and we can see what man's behaviour might have been
if he had developed along lines followed by some of our close
relatives among the higher primates. It is rare to find an
area of biological inquiry in which there are so many perfect
experimental controls and natural parallels. We should make
the best possible use of it.

Each of us eats about one thousand meals a year. By the
time we have swallowed twenty or thirty thousand, we tend
naturally to regard ourselves as experts on the subject of
eating. But, intensive as the experience may be, it is rarely
enough to give us a proper understanding of the game. To
become true aficionados, we need to know the backgrounds of
the foods and the feeders.

In the beginning, there was nothing to eat and nobody to eat
it. Just an embryonic planet in orbit around a second-magnitude

star. How it got there is immaterial, but it is certain that at one time it was too hot to support life of any kind. Then it cooled and developed an envelope of captive gases – an atmosphere. In this early atmosphere were hydrogen, methane, water vapour and ammonia. Four inorganic gases which, if provided with a source of energy such as an electric spark, combine to form organic compounds called amino acids. This simple experiment, which can be reproduced in any school laboratory, shows how lightning storms in the primitive atmosphere built organic molecules and washed them down into the ancient seas. All we need to do now is to add a pinch of ultraviolet light, bring it to a boil, and there it is – primeval soup. Stir gently for many millions of years, and the soup thickens as the molecules group together and react with each other to form even more complex substances such as carbohydrates or sugars. These were the first foods.

The first feeders came a little later, produced by the action of enzymes and complicated biochemistry from the early carbohydrates and proteins. The food made the feeder, who promptly made more food to make more feeders. And so it all began. For a time things went splendidly, but then the first feeders met their first snag. They discovered hunger. There were so many of them that the soup could not feed them all and some had to die. The others, the fitter ones, survived and invented natural selection.

So, long before the development of the gut, the game had already begun. It continued in this way until one group of feeders discovered photosynthesis (putting together by light) and were able to make direct use of the energy in the sun. These 'light-eaters' were very successful and gave rise to all green plants, but as none of them take an active part in the game, they need not concern us here. One thing they did do, however, was to release oxygen into the oceans and the air. This made respiration possible and opened the way for a new generation of souped-up soup eaters who were able to get more out of their food.

At this stage, two distinct styles began to develop. Some early feeders went out to get their food, while others preferred to wait for the food to come to them. Those that chose to play at home enjoyed the security of operating from a fixed home base. Those that played an away game had the advantage of a wider selection of foods. This turned out to be more important in the long run. The away teams were forced to develop mechanisms for going away. They came up with hairlike structures which stuck out from the cell wall and flapped to move them along. These *cilia*, with little modification, now form the light-sensitive cells in our retinas and the motion-detecting hairs in our inner ears. Mobility exposed the fragile cells to the danger of accidental damage, and so, for mutual protection, they took to moving around in groups. In time members of the group developed different functions. Some took on the task of protecting themselves and all the other members of the group as well. This division of labour made it possible for the cells concerned with feeding to organise themselves into an association that could deal with much more complex foods. This was the first gut.

It was a simple saclike structure to start with, but it quickly grew more complex as the whole organism developed. All the mobile feeders adopted a simple cylindrical shape that was easy to move and presented as little surface to the environment as possible. The cylinder was modified according to the needs of each animal and equipped with a variety of openings and appendages. The exact nature of these depended very largely on the way these gut containers played the game.

One of the best ways to get some idea of the variety of feeding adaptations which appeared is to look at all the techniques that man thinks he invented. The greatest advantage of the human species is that it has managed to retain a fairly generalised shape that can be adapted to do almost anything. The only structure that has become specialised is the brain, and man uses this to compensate for all his physical short-comings. He invents tools and techniques and uses them as extensions of his simple body to help him find and catch his food. To him these are new, but to nature they are not. For every human invention there is a natural counterpart.

Man started by using clubs and daggers and spears to help

him hunt, but there was certainly nothing new in these. They were usually borrowed directly from the animals around him. The limb bone, perhaps even with a sharp hoof attached, became a club and the sabre tooth of the tiger served as dagger and gouge. The horns of antelope, such as oryx, became swords, and the jawbone with its row of sharp teeth was a knife. Later man made his implements from stone and metal, but they were still directly influenced by these early animal prototypes. To compensate for his own lack of speed, man had to give speed to his weapons, so he produced aerodynamic swords and daggers. He made harpoons and arrows. But even in this he was not alone. One of the first developments of the early multicells was a sting cell that flung a barbed projectile that could even penetrate the hard shell of a crab. The human archer was preceded by the archer fish which has a mouth modified to spit missiles of water with great accuracy at insects flying several feet above the surface. Man gave his projectiles more power by coating them with poison, but this was a direct crib from the snake.

Man produced hooks and harpoons to help him fish. The fish themselves have swords and saws, and every curved claw is a natural hook. The line attached to the hook is, once again, to compensate for man's physical inability to get close enough to apply the hook in person. The principle of baiting the hook with a lure is one long since developed by the angler fish which dangles an attractive luminous lure above its cavernous mouth. Man invented the fishnet just 400,000,000 years after the larva of the caddis fly stretched a silk net between two stones in a stream. Fish traps have long been used even by plants such as the bladderwort; pit traps by the ant lion larva which digs craters to catch ants; and spring traps by every animal which has teeth to hold a struggling prey.

Man dreamed up the lasso but was beaten to it by the chameleon's tongue and by a spider which hurls a line of web at insects flying by. Man cooperated to corner herds of animals in box canyons; barracuda chase shoals of small fish into shallow bays and pen them in while they feed at their leisure. When it comes to locating prey, the sonar apparatus fitted to trawlers is a hundred times more cumbersome and not half as efficient as the one used by dolphins. The sniperscope sights attached to modern rifles for hunting at night are long antedated by the pineal eye of some adders that is sensitive to infra-red light. There are some animal systems of feeding which man, with all his technology, has still not been able to emulate. Fishing bats are able to use their radar system from the air to detect fish underwater – something submarine hunters would dearly love to know how to do.

Many of these are adaptations made by aquatic animals, but some are clearly not. The first feeders lived in the water, but as soon as they got together and developed team spirit they were able to come up for air. A single cell directly absorbs food and water and oxygen from its surroundings. It needs to be surrounded by water in order to survive. Unicells did very well in the primeval soup and the sea, but to colonise land they had to group together into closed systems that maintained their own liquid interiors. In this internal environment each cell still has its own 'waterfront', but the organism as a whole is free to live in liquid or gas. Free to move out into the air and take advantage of an entirely new feeding situation. The new habitat was necessarily a much drier one, and the organisms had to make special provisions to combat water loss. But it was inevitable that some loss would occur and, as this had to be made good, a new goal was added to the game. The acquisition of water – or drinking. This must also be considered as part of the complex of feeding behaviour.

There are some special feeding adaptations designed to deal with water, but the primary goal is the food itself. In a sense the ultimate aim of the game is the content of the food. The carbohydrates, fats, proteins, minerals, vitamins and roughage that it contains. But none of these things can really be considered as legitimate aims or search images. With the exception of weight-conscious humans, no feeder deliberately sets out to find a mineral or a fat to feed on. He may be driven by a physiological need to add protein to his diet, but he sees it as a locust or a tasty leg of lamb. I intend therefore to ignore the nutritional and biochemical qualities of food and to concentrate only on those external characteristics or *sign stimuli* which give food its value to the feeder.

As each feeder became bodily or behaviourally adapted to his favourite food evolutionary links were forged between them. These were often two-way links producing a kind of feedback in which the feeder influenced the food. Some foods became negatively adapted to their feeders by developing modifications that helped prevent them from being eaten. All types of camouflage are 'unfeeding' adaptations. Some moths, for instance, avoid birds' beaks by growing cryptic colours that match the bark of trees on which they sit during the day. Other adaptations are designed to reveal rather than conceal. A few moths have false warning signals that give them huge eye markings like a frightening bird of prey.

All these relationships between species fit into what ecologists call a food chain. But the name is misleading as it implies that there is only a linear connection between the foods and their feeders. It is true that plant juice is sucked by lice, which are eaten by spiders, which are caught by warblers, which in turn fall prey to hawks. But warblers do not live exclusively on lice; they also eat flies and fruit. Hawks sometimes vary their diet by catching mice and lizards. There is an intricate web of relationships in any community that would be far better described in terms of something like a *food lattice*.

The higher up the lattice we climb, the more complex it becomes. Balancing on the top is the latest top species – the most remarkable species this planet has ever known. Man is so far above the other species that he is stepping out into space, but he is still very much part of this planet. He was born here into a family of other animals which show a lot of family resemblance.

All the family take part in the game. Even the babies play, imitating the patterns of their parents, training to keep fit because it is a game in which only the fittest survive. Man alone has learned to play the game so well that he can afford to field a professional team to take part on behalf of the whole species. The rest of us are amateurs, part-time players free just to sit and watch or to play some other game. I have decided to become a gamekeeper, giving a running commentary and analysing the present state of play.

I hope to show that the game of eating is fundamental to life and that it has influenced almost every aspect of living. All of us used to be full-time players, and we have carried the tricks we learned in the game over into other aspects of our lives. Just as a sleeping dog goes through all the motions of running down and killing a rabbit, even salivating in the process, so we unwittingly demonstrate patterns of feeding in non-feeding situations. And in the process of feeding itself, we behave in ways which provide dramatic evidence of our animal origins and of the way in which we came to be human.

So, on with the game.

TWO

FEEDERS

Imagine an ape with savage fangs in enormous, powerful jaws. An animal with long muscular arms ending in a set of vicious claws. A killer with an uncanny ability to anticipate every movement of its prey, to creep up in the dark and slay without a sound.

It sounds like something in a horror film that comes out of the jungle to take over the world. And that is just what it might have done. When our ancestors came down from the trees to make a new life for themselves in the open, they could have gone in any direction. They could have become totally insectivorous, gone burrowing in anthills, grown great digging claws, and lost their teeth. They could have developed a passion for roots and shoots and grown an armour-plated skin. Or they could have gone into competition with the other predators.

We now know that many of them did become beasts of prey. For those that did, there were several further possibilities. They could concentrate on killing birds and small mammals, or they could go after the really big prizes. They could develop along the same lines as the big cats, or they could try a new and entirely different approach. If they chose to copy the cats, the result would have been something like that monster ape. There might well have been such an experiment, but fortunately for us it failed. It was our line of development – the use of tools to catch and kill – that turned out to be the most successful.

There are stories in central Africa of a killer ape that the local people call chemosit or nandi. It is said to have an enormous head and a sloping body ending in a completely bare rump. It is just possible that such an animal could have escaped scientific notice, but if the killer ape ever existed, we are more likely to find it as a fossil. Our knowledge of ancient primates is far from complete. There are many gaps that could contain a cat ape or an anteater ape or even a grazing ape. Evolutionary experiments that failed to produce a successful line or to leave evidence where we could easily find it.

The whole class of mammals are comparatively recent arrivals, but they already have a considerable fossil background. There are fourteen orders of mammals that only have extinct representatives. Each surviving order has almost as many dead as living species, and we have literally only begun to scrape the surface of the fossil sites. The picture that emerges from these is one of explosive experimentation. Of a force so strong that every possibility has to be investigated. Most fail, but there is usually one approach to each problem that works well. One man's poison is another man's meat. We are the results of one successful experiment in the flesh. Or, more precisely, out of the flesh.

Man is what he is and does what he does because he once was a killer. He was hungry and needed food, and the food he most wanted was meat. So he applied his growing brain to the problem of killing – and started a chain of circumstances that still affects our lives today. Because our ancestors needed greater speed, they became more upright and today we have vertical men. Because they needed artificial weapons, tools were developed and today we have an elaborate instrumentation. Because cooperation was essential, their brains became even more complex and a language and a culture came into being. Today we also have spinal disorders, ballistic missiles and racial disturbances, but we have had to take the bad with the good. Both were produced by our diet.

The same applies to all the other feeders. The food they ate, or wanted to eat, has made them what they are today. For simple organisms like bacteria, food means oil or garden soil. Where foods are simple, adaptations to them can be equally simple. But for things like snails and nightingales, food means much more elaborate living substances. Complex foods need complex adaptations and produce complex feeders. Man is the most complicated of all, and it will help understand him if we look at similar feeding patterns in other less complicated animals. But we will have to choose these species carefully.

We could start by rearranging the whole zoological kingdom according to the kind of food each animal most often eats. Such a classification would not be entirely arbitrary because taxonomists often use characteristics that animals have acquired as a result of concentrating on a particular food. They classify some mammals, for instance, entirely on the shape and size of their teeth. This is a perfectly valid procedure because the taxonomist is comparing only those animals which he has already taken care to isolate from all others on the grounds that they have warm blood, hair, live young and a four-chambered heart. In deciding which species can be usefully compared to man, we have to exercise the same kind of caution.

Apparent similarities can occur purely as a result of convergence. Vampire bats and mosquitoes both use sharp mouth parts to puncture the skin of sleeping animals, both produce a secretion that prevents clotting, and both fly away afterwards laden with blood. This sort of similarity is interesting because it shows how the need for one kind of food can push two completely different animals in the same direction, but it is not evidence of an affinity between them. Nothing can be gained by comparing the species. We will have to be careful not to make the same mistake with man. There is a Mediterranean ant which collects seeds, allows them to germinate, and then sun-bakes a kind of biscuit from the dough. It is very tempting to draw an analogy between this procedure and the baking techniques of early farming man. There are marked similarities which indicate the sort of sequence that might have been involved in man's discovery of the process, but it would be very risky to draw any direct comparisons. Man and the ant are too far apart.

Homo sapiens is the last surviving species of the Hominid family that is classified with the families of apes and monkeys in the suborder of the Anthropoids. All these are included with the lemurs and tarsiers in the order of the primates. This order, Primata, is just one of many that enjoy milk secreted from mammary glands and have been grouped together in the class Mammalia. These are our closest relatives. These are the species with which we can begin to be compared. So, in this chapter and in the rest of the book, we will concentrate on the similarities and differences between man and the other mammals.

Mammals began about 150,000,000 years ago as a splinter group breaking away from the cold-blooded world of the reptiles. They started by developing a more efficient, more sensitive body, a complex brain, constant high temperature, athletic limbs, fewer offspring with longer dependence on their parents and – most important of all – intelligence. In spite of these improvements, they were subject to the dictatorship of the giant reptiles and were forced to hide away in nooks and crannies for another 80,000,000 years.

But they were not idle in exile. To start with, they had teeth like their reptilian ancestors. Long rows of small sharp, unspecialised teeth useful only for gripping odds and ends of food and breaking them up a bit before swallowing. Like their scaly antecedents, they lived mainly on insects. But, unlike the reptiles from which they evolved, early mammals were warm-blooded and more nocturnal. Moving about at night, when the reptiles were torpid, they had the chance to try other kinds of food – varieties of fruits and grasses, the odd piece of carrion or fish, and the even more exciting array of insects that came out after dark.

Right from the start, they had to compete with each other for these new foods, and it was not long before some developed special attributes which gave them an advantage over the others. The carrion eaters grew tearing teeth to help them deal with dead meat and later got to grips with live meat by evolving strong, killing claws and powerful necks and jaws. The munchers of leaves and grass grew better munching teeth and long, involved digestive organs to make the best of poor-quality food. Those partial to ants grew digging claws and long sticky tongues and forgot about their teeth. And the fish fanciers became streamlined swimmers with sharp conical teeth for holding tight their slippery prey. By the time the ruling reptiles began to lose their grip the mammals had multiplied into such a formidable array that they were easily able to seize the throne. They took it in their teeth. Teeth that had been modified to deal with a whole new range of foods and that made it possible for them to spread out in all directions and invade the air, the trees, the plains, the swamps, the rivers and the sea. The reptiles were eaten out of existence.

First of the mammals to begin gnawing away at reptilian authority were the insect eaters. Little archi-mammals which crept around at night, catching bugs and things in their simple triangular teeth. They did not pose any direct threat to the dinosaurs, but they were the base from which the mammalian assault was made.

Today we still have insectivores which show many of the anatomical and behavioural patterns of their forefeeders. These include moles, shrews and hedgehogs. Most living forms still concentrate mainly on insects, but a few very successful species have gone on to eat whatever they can lay their primitive hands on. These include omnivores (anything-eaters) like the opossum – one of the few marsupials to survive side by side with modern mammals. One group of insect eaters persevered with their invertebrate diet for a long time and only fairly recently changed their menus – the fruit- and nectar-eating bats. They are now herbivores and living examples of what happened about 60,000,000 years ago when the insectivore stock split to give rise to two large groups of deviants. These were the herbivores and the carnivores.

Right from the start, the herbivores developed along three distinct lines. Some grazed, some browsed, and some took to picking fruit. Among the grass eaters are horses and cattle. The second line – the leaf and twig eaters – includes tapir, elephant and some kinds of deer. A few of these browsers have taken to supplementing their diet with fruits and nuts, but there is one group of herbivores that took to fruit picking right away and never gave it up. In this third category are the majority of monkeys and apes. All are mainly herbivorous, feeding largely on leaves or fruit. They might occasionally take an insect or even kill and eat a small bird or mammal. Only one group of herbivores eats everything regularly. These are the pigs, whose teeth have now become so generalised that they are often confused with our own.

The second group to break away from the insect-eating stock at an early age was the carnivores – the flesh feeders. More than any other group, they illustrate dramatically how choice of food influences development. The changes are best seen in the teeth. A typical set of early mammalian teeth included incisors at the front of the mouth for cutting, canines below the eyes for tearing and slashing, and premolars and molars at the back of the mouth for grinding. The first flesh feeders changed this arrangement to suit their new diet by lengthening the canines for more efficient killing and by giving the grinding teeth a notched cutting edge like a carving knife. Others went on to live in the water where they needed to grab their prey rather than slash it. They reduced the size of the canine and developed instead a set of traplike teeth that could hold onto even the most slippery food. Some, who needed to crack large bones to get at the marrow, developed powerful jaws with teeth that were much more robust. A few kept on eating insects and kept their simple teeth. And one or two gave up eating meat altogether and developed the flat grinding teeth of herbivores.

Most modern flesh eaters are 'pure' carnivores, like hyenas and cats. The nonconformists include the aardwolf, which eats insects and has reacquired the old tooth pattern, and the giant panda, which is now a browser. But, most important of all, there are species such as bears, raccoons and badgers which eat absolutely anything.

One thing is immediately apparent in this classification by food. There are no animals which started off as omnivores. But in each of the three main groups there are some species that begin to go in for everything-eating. And, in every case, the broader diet has had the effect of broadening their horizons. All the omnivorous feeders occur in a wide variety of tropical and temperate areas, instead of being restricted to the one part of the world where their original foods were found. From typical insectivore stock came the bats, mobile not only because they can fly but because of the wide range of their habitats and adaptations. Today there are a thousand different species including fruit-eating, nectar-licking and blood-sucking bats, as well as the original insect eaters. From the flesh specialists, each with its own restricted habitat, came the bears. Omnivorous ex-meat eaters with the ability also to eat fruits, berries, fish and honey and to distribute themselves all over North America, Europe and Asia. From the grazers, browsers and fruit pickers strayed one animal which could do all three – and take a little meat on the side – the pig. Today there are pigs in every continent, except Australia, and even there they breed profusely if given the chance to escape from domesticity.

The trend among these pioneers is towards an increasing ability to live on an increasingly large variety of foods. It is a trend encouraged by the fact that the omnivores are stimulated by their varied fare to a higher level of intellectual activity, a level which makes them the feeders most likely to survive. And the fittest of all the feeders – the most omnivorous of all the developing omnivores – is a species that has undergone three dietary developments. The only animal ever to move from insect eating to fruit picking to meat eating to eating absolutely anything. Man.

The complex dietary development of mammals can be summarised in this way:
1. ALL mammals once were insect eaters:
   Some still are . . . for example, the moles.
2. MANY mammals underwent a SINGLE dietary change:
   From insectivore to herbivore . . . the deer.
   From insectivore to carnivore . . . the cats.
   From insectivore to omnivore . . . the opossum.
3. A FEW mammals went through a SECOND change:
   From herbivore to supercarnivore . . . the ape-men.
   From herbivore to superomnivore . . . the pigs.

From carnivore to superinsectivore . . . the aardwolf.
From carnivore to superherbivore . . . the giant panda.
From carnivore to superomnivore . . . the bears.
4.   ONLY ONE mammal made a THIRD change of diet:
     From supercarnivore to total omnivore . . . man.

Man is so obviously unique in this evolutionary series that it is
necessary to follow his development in detail. This is the time
sequence:

150,000,000 years ago	INSECTIVORE	First mammals
60,000,000	HERBIVORE	First carnivores and herbivores First omnivores
30,000,000		Ancestor leaves trees and extends diet
20,000,000		First scavengers to use tools
3,000,000	SUPER-CARNIVORE	Ape-man walks erect and becomes first hunter to use tools
500,000		Peking man uses fire
50,000		Neanderthal man uses more complex tools
30,000	TOTAL OMNIVORE	Cro-Magnon man with refined technology and complete diet
10,000		Agricultural revolution and first farmers
200		Industrial revolution and first men who neither find nor grow their food

Man's story begins in Africa about 30,000,000 years ago. At this time a primate lived on the edge of the forest near the open bushy grassland. We know very little about him except that his teeth were fairly simple with features that suggest he was ancestral to both man and the modern apes. Then there is a gap in the record and the next discoveries date back about 20,000,000 years. These include fossils from Egypt and East Africa, of which some are much more apelike and some are clearly becoming human.

Both types of animal were still capable of climbing but had come down from the trees and were spending more time in the open. By doing so, they automatically increased the range of their diet. Baboons which live in the same areas today eat leaves, berries, bulbs, insects, scorpions, centipedes and lizards and are known to capture young antelope. The pioneer terrestrial primates must have enjoyed somewhat similar fare which helped make them independent of the trees. They were able to range over a far wider area and come into contact with all sorts of problems their tree-living ancestors knew nothing about. One of these was the fierce competition for attractive foods. Each group of ground-living mammals had some special feeding pattern which made certain they got their share, but the pioneer primates had none. They lacked the complex digestive system necessary for eating grass and were forced for a long time to live as scavengers and collectors.

In time a few took the plunge and followed the only road to high-protein food. They began to explore carnivory. By virtue of having lived in the trees, they already had efficient grasping hands and good distance-judging eyes in the front of their faces. The combination of these characteristics made it possible for them to pick up strange objects and examine them carefully – a habit which encouraged the development of a large, inquiring brain. Being apes, they also had some sort of communal life and already practised a measure of cooperation. With these advantages, and very little else, they entered a strange new world and went into direct competition with the already efficiently adapted professional killers.

What happened then is something we still have to guess but it

seems likely that they became faster runners with better hands
and bigger brains. They must have suffered considerably but
they triumphed, because about 3,000,000 years ago a group
of much less apelike animals walked proudly erect in the open
country of southeast Africa. The most interesting thing about
these ape-men is that their remains are often found in conjunction
with great piles of animal bones. Large carnivores might have
been responsible for collecting all these bones in the caves, but
the way in which the fragments have been broken and marked
suggests it was the ape-men who were responsible.

The pygmies and aborigines of today live on tubers and roots,
fruits and seeds, nuts and pods, honey, mushrooms, beetles and
larvae, as well as meat. The ape-men probably had a similarly
mixed diet, but soft foods unfortunately leave no trace. The
evidence of the bones however provides us with some good
clues to the feeding habits of these early hunters. They severed
antelope limbs for use as clubs and bludgeoned their prey to
death. We do not know if they killed all the animals whose remains
are found in the caves, but they made a special habit of bringing
back heads from which they extracted and ate the brains. They
also split open the long bones to get at the marrow.

The ape-man was poorly equipped for killing. So, before
making his own kills, he must have got his meat by beating
the jackals to it. Our ancestors were just clean-up men but
only as an intermediate stage in the climb to higher things.
Most animals develop on the principle of body adaptation, but
they developed by a process of body elimination. Instead of
growing great canine teeth or learning to run and climb quickly,
they renounced their bodies and developed tools for offence
and defence. But even with these, the ape-man on his own
was at a disadvantage. To hunt successfully, he needed skill
and resource. He also badly needed help. So groups of hunters
joined together.

Cooperation between separate individuals, and possibly between separate groups of hunters, created the need for a more
complex and advanced signal system. The ape-man's ancestors
used a complicated visual language of facial expression and body
posture. This was fine for a life of individual food gathering, but

it was not nearly sophisticated enough for a life of social cooperation. Some new means of expression had to be found, and language – a vocal language in its simplest form – was the result. There was cohesion within a group during the killing process and during the sharing of the kill. There would also be a period of social contact when the members were sitting around comfortably filled after the meal. These were excellent opportunities for practising and perfecting the new type of communication. Opportunities which would never have been given to a similar form which was grass- or insect-eating.

The habit of feeding on flesh undoubtedly accelerated the ape-man's development. Because he followed the grass-eating herds and became less sedentary in nature, he extended his range and came into contact with other groups which were similarly occupied. Sometimes they fought – we know that they ate each other – but at other times they intermingled and exchanged ideas. This too gave an impetus to evolution.

The next steps in the making of man are once again obscured by lack of information. It is almost impossible to build up a complete picture on such scanty evidence as we have at the moment. If all the remains of early man discovered all over the world were assembled, they would scarcely fill a coffin. Lacking evidence, we can only assume that after taking his first car- nivorous steps in Africa, he went quickly on to learn new tricks in new areas. We know that half a million years ago, a toolmaker was harrying the deer and accumulating vast piles of bones in the caves of eastern Asia. This was Peking man.

We call him man instead of ape-man for several reasons. One is that he made and used stone tools. A number of crude chopper and flake instruments have been found in the caves, and there is clear evidence that he built hearths and used that very important tool – fire. The fossil finds also include skulls with braincases broken open from the bottom with some skill. It seems probable that the brains, and the missing bodies, were eaten. Eaten by Peking man himself, because there is no trace of any other animal that could have been capable of this precise manipulation.

We now have a tool-making, cannibalistic, fire-using man in

Asia (and also in Africa) half a million years ago. His ability to control fire was soon put to good use because his advent was closely followed by four periods of intense glaciation. There are several fossil finds that fit into the early ice days, but we have to go to the third interglacial period to find evidence of a marked change in diet. Here, 50,000 years ago, we find a man with heavy, protruding jaws and eyebrows and a large brain. Neanderthal man, who sought shelter from the cold in caves, used fire a great deal and manufactured a variety of tools. The fact that the right hand of several skeletons has been shown to be larger than the left indicates that he was right-handed and therefore must have been endowed with considerable manipulative skill. He made tools for dressing skins and fire-hardened wooden spears that were used in hunting.

The Neanderthals were nomads. They followed the large herds of game, killing these when they could and, when they couldn't, playing jackal to the sabre-toothed tiger. They were still largely dependent on red meat, and with the onset of the cold and the lack of sunshine, they began to suffer from a deficiency of vitamins C and D. Their skeletons show evidence of rickets, dental decay and rheumatism – all consequences of dietary deficiencies. As a result, the men were unable to hunt well. The women had poor bone structure and great difficulty in childbirth, and the infant mortality rate must have been very high.

As the last ice age neared its end 20,000 years ago, the Neanderthal people were on the verge of extinction. They were given the final push by a new race of people who came pouring in from the east. These invaders were superior in almost every respect. They knew more, talked together, and hunted the same foods with improved methods and greater success. Their superiority lay in increased intelligence and more advanced technology, but most of all in an improved diet. They were still hunters but were so successful at it that they had the time to develop other interests. They fished and trapped, and their women were skilled at gathering and preparing fruits and cereals and grubs. The wheel came full circle from insectivore to herbivore to supercarnivore and back again to herbivore and insectivore. The feeder who closed the cycle by becoming the first total omnivore was Cro-Magnon man. His origins are obscure; we know only that he came from somewhere in central Asia, but he was a true man – the first to be called *Homo sapiens*. This is the species to which we belong, so from now on, we're talking about ourselves.

We owe a great deal to the fact that our development was determined by these drastic changes in diet. It was necessary for the conservative arboreal herbivore to go on a riotously carnivorous splurge before it could become a sapient terrestrial omnivore. By enduring the rigours of the chase, we have stolen a march on our cousins, the apes. They never had a carnivorous phase, and, as a result, their numbers are dwindling every year. Ours are multiplying in an alarming fashion.

Man's superiority in the game of eating is absolute. There is no other species which eats so many different things in so many different ways. There is no organic substance that some man somewhere has not regarded as food. This catholic appetite has played a big part in human evolution and may have a bigger part yet to play. The environment has always been variable. With our help it is becoming very fickle indeed. There is a real danger that we will succeed in changing it so much that it will be completely unsuitable for our own survival. This has happened before. In ecological succession, one stage is followed by another containing completely different species. A plant that needs soil with little nitrogen moves into a suitable area; it thrives and does so well that it rapidly increases the nitrogen content in the soil to a point where it can no longer survive. It has been destroyed by its own success and is soon replaced by species that are better adapted to the new conditions. The first plants do not become extinct because their seeds have been spread into new areas where the whole process can begin again.

But what about man? If our environment changes too much, there is nowhere else to go. It is pointless to think in terms of moving to another planet. At the moment it takes a major effort by a whole nation to put only two of its members onto a nearby satellite for a few hours. With well over 60,000,000 babies already being born each year, we will never even be able to send our seed into space. The only hope is for man to adapt himself to meet changes in the environment here. And the ability to make such adaptations is one that is kept alive by our flexible diet.

There is nothing more indicative of an evolutionary end point than a specialised diet. An animal specialised for feeding on ants or eucalyptus leaves may live well for a while. But it has run headlong into a cul-de-sac from which there is no escape, and no chance of survival once the food is finished. For an omnivore the failure of one food source is nothing more than a temporary inconvenience. He simply goes on to try out something else. Man is the most omnivorous of all and has done this many times. We even feel the need to explore before there is any need. This is what it means to be an omnivore.

The human species as a whole is successful because it is omnivorous. Individual members however show a complete range of feeding habits which includes examples from all the categories. Nomadic food gatherers rely heavily on insects. When desert locusts are available, the Bushmen of the Kalahari eat nothing else. Australian aborigines spend a lot of time searching out the moth and beetle larvae they call witchetties. Human desire for insect food is sometimes so strong that it might have provided the impetus for one of our greatest achievements – the invention of stone tools. How else can a man, without claws or hoofs, get into rock-hard termite hills?

There are some groups of men who eat nothing but meat. Eskimos survive on a diet composed entirely of whale and walrus, seal and polar bear. Like other carnivores, they get their vitamins by eating the stomach contents of their prey, but even this does not seem to be necessary. A famous Arctic explorer once tried living on a pure meat diet for a whole year. The experiment was done under medical supervision, and he showed no ill effects whatsoever. In contrast to the meat eaters are a growing band of vegetarians. Most of these still eat eggs and milk and cheese and should really be classified as omnivores, but there are a few religious sects that are completely herbivorous. Man lacks the long gut and the gut fauna that help true herbivores break down plant cellulose, so there are biological limits to which a vegetable diet can be taken. Some involuntary vegetarians are forced past this limit and into starvation.

Insectivore, herbivore and carnivore people are a natural part of the spectrum that makes our species omnivorous. All have their counterparts among the other mammals. But there is one further aspect of the total omnivore that has no parallel in the animal world. It has never happened before. This is the supermarket syndrome. It is produced by the professional team that we pay to play the game – and by the fact that management of this team is placed in fewer and fewer hands. Never in the field of human evolution was so much fed to so many by so few. The products of the few are being more and more widely distributed and are sweeping away local differences and individual preferences. One man's meat is in everyone's mouth and is producing a dull continuity that masquerades under the title of international cuisine. People in any one place probably have access to as many different foods as before, but they are the same foods that are available in every other place. The symptoms of the syndrome are an increasing unwillingness to prepare one's own food, an ignorance of the techniques involved, a reliance on an ever-dwindling variety of foods, an offhand attitude to the whole question of eating, and a loss of curiosity about foods that have never before been tried. The result of this is a loss of omnivority – a disease that we could call univority. It is a disease that is highly contagious and could be fatal.

If a broad appetite and an insatiable curiosity about food can make a man, then a loss of these qualities can break him. It is no accident that inquiring minds so often rest on sensitive and curious palates. Now that we suddenly have the ability to direct our own evolution, we need those kinds of minds more than ever. If food can help produce them, it must be helped to do so. But we can plan nothing until we understand the process more thoroughly.

THREE

FINDING FOOD

For modern men, finding food is not particularly difficult – unless the refrigerator is empty and the shops and restaurants are closed. This happens, but not often enough to be a major problem. In our sophisticated version of the game, the professionals find or grow the food and deliver it to us. Most people have never been faced with the problem of having to go out and hunt for food in the wild. But we are all products of animals which did have to do this, and even the most urban among us still have parts of that inheritance.

A univore – an animal which eats only one kind of food – has no need to explore. The koala, for instance, lives right in the middle of its pantry. It needs no special hunting pattern for tracking its food down and no special mechanism for recognising it when it sees it. A gum leaf is a gum leaf. But for man the problem has always been much more difficult. To start with, we were insect eaters. Most insectivores are small and active and need to eat almost continuously to stay alive. Shrews eat their own weight in food each day, and, to find this much, they have to know exactly where to look. An insect eater therefore has to be fairly exploratory.

Insects come in such an enormous number of shapes and sizes, some of which taste bad or are even poisonous, that it is important to be able to distinguish between them. The position is made even more complicated by the fact that some harmless species pretend to be lethal by imitating the harmful ones. So it is vital for a successful insectivore to be able not only to track his food down efficiently but also to recognise the small differences which separate one species from another.

A few of the insect eaters accomplish both these tasks by using their sense of smell. A male moth can detect a female of its species many miles away by a chemical substance the female releases into the air. There is no doubt that many mammals follow the same trails to their food. Anteaters have nostrils right at the tip of their elongated nose, and they certainly make use of them when hunting in the dark. They can even smell the difference between soldier and worker ants in the same nest. Another cue may be sound. A great deal of communication between insects is carried on by sound. The whine of a mosquito, the buzz of a cicada, the chirp of a cricket all advertise the presence of an insect in search of a mate. The volume and pitch of the call are determined by a compromise between the conflicting needs of the animal to reveal its presence to a potential mate and to conceal itself from a potential predator. The result of the conflict is usually a nice balance between the two – just enough insects surviving to breed and keep the species going. But some predators have tried to tip the balance a little farther in their favour by developing extra-sensitivity. Bats have so refined their system of locating insects by the sounds they make that they can find them even when they are silent. Experiments have shown that a bat can use its sonar system to distinguish between two similar species of flying insects at a range of fifteen feet.

Man never developed a built-in radar, but his prehuman experience as an insect eater exposed him to problems like these. In solving the problems he had to improvise, and one of his improvisations led to a change of diet. He continued to eat insects, but became predominantly herbivorous. Yet, despite this change, he never became a typical herbivore.

True herbivores are divided into grazers and browsers. The grazers tend to be large and not very intelligent. They live on a limited number of plants that happen to be common in their habitat. When these become less common, the animals follow-my-leader off along a well-beaten track to new grazing grounds. This sort of life does not require a high exploratory drive. The browsers need to know more about their environment because they feed on a wider variety of foods, some of which may even be poisonous at certain times. They are more intelligent than the grazers, but equally specialised. Man developed so quickly, and along such general lines, that he bypassed the dead ends of specialised grazing and browsing and went straight in for a fruit and nut way of life.

This required more opportunism. Monkeys which still live in this way today do not necessarily cover great distances in their search for food, but they need to know their home area very well indeed in order to find all the food there. Not having a staple food that is always plentiful, they have to take advantage of fruits in season, mushrooms when they grow, insects that pass by – whatever happens to be available at the time. Their need to explore the world around them is high and persistent. Ours was too.

There is no question of herbivores having to capture their prey but they certainly need to be able to recognise it. Some, such as the rodents, have enormous menus which may include several hundred different food items in the course of a normal year. They must be able to appreciate the differences between foods in order to decide which to eat now and which to put away for later – and perhaps even which not to eat at all. A great deal of work has been done on the food habits of wild and captive rodents. Most of this is anecdotal and provides us only with a list of what is eaten, but some studies have been observational.

I have worked with rats, mice, hamsters, gerbils, voles, acouchies, chipmunks, squirrels and prairie marmots and have found that all these animals exercise an active preference in their selection of food. They respond to shape, size, colour, pattern, weight, texture, flavour and smell. The more opportunist species make the finer distinctions and are actively attracted to unfamiliar food objects. Chipmunks sort rapidly through a pile of food, eating the soft fragrant foods on the spot, hanging the moist ones up to dry, burying the smooth, hard foods underground, and taking the really strange ones home to examine in safety. I have seen wild rat nests with stones, coins and screws in them – all clearly retrieved to be considered at leisure as potential sources of food. The fact that there was only one of each in any nest indicated that the rats found these objects wanting and decided to ignore them in the future.

Each species has its own distinct preferences which may vary according to the immediate use to which the food is being put. The acouchy (a long-legged relative of the guinea pig) chooses dark-coloured foods when it is hungry and, perhaps because they are less likely to be diseased, light-coloured objects when it is busy hoarding. Other species show what seem to be meaningless, though completely consistent, individual preferences for particular shapes and colours.

Individual prairie marmots are particularly idiosyncratic. One will prefer bright, smooth food objects; another will always choose rough, heavy ones with a strong smell; and a third will head straight for those that are small and light with a mild flavour. In an individual these preferences seem pointless, but marmots are intensely social, and, taken altogether, their personal tastes make sense. They form an excellent social mechanism which ensures that a colony exploits all the food resources available to it and does not damage its habitat by stripping it of only one kind of food. This is the sort of behaviour that makes the non-specialist species so successful.

At a higher level, among the monkeys and apes, there is even more striking evidence of selective food gathering. These species live primarily in the trees, where sight is far more important than smell. It is not surprising, therefore, to find that they respond to very subtle visual stimuli. In searching for food, the colours of fruits are helpful clues, and most monkeys have evolved good colour vision to take advantage of these. Their food is motionless, so they have developed the sort of visual acuity which makes it possible for them to recognise small differences in shape, size and pattern. Their sense of taste is equally refined and has been produced in response to a diet which is highly flavoured. Because fruit becomes sweeter when it is ripe and ready for eating, we still tend to choose sweet foods in preference to all others. We have this sweet tooth as a souvenir of the days when we lived in the same fruit-picking way.

Success in the fruit business led our ancestors out to the grassland, where they turned into foragers. Each individual had to search for roots and shoots, fruits and nuts, insects and eggs. If he failed to find enough, he died. There was no question of food being shared. Protoman was still in an uncooperative stage and living, literally, from hand to mouth. This every-feeder-for-himself way of life produced a high degree of self-reliance and a powerful search urge in every individual. It was an urge so strong that it still exists today.

Children all over the world play their own versions of hide-and-seek and hunt the thimble. Adults hold treasure hunts. Some of the hunts are real – in search of pirate gold or sunken galleons. They attract a vast horde of people with spades and cryptic charts and metal detectors. Now and then someone finds something valuable, but the returns hardly ever justify the expense and the time and effort involved. There must be some other reward. Anyone who has ever been involved in excavation work will know what a wonderful sensation it is to pick up a Roman coin or to uncover a piece of fossil bone. The fact that these finds are very often worthless in no way detracts from the excitement. Even experienced naturalists get a kick out of finding a bird's nest with eggs in it – and there is no need for them to be hungry or intent on studying the bird concerned. There is reward simply in the act of finding some-thing, regardless of its value. The coin we pick up in the street means far more to us than the twenty we already have in our pocket. All these are manifestations of a deep-seated urge we have to search for things – an urge we owe to our scavenging forefathers.

We no longer have to search for food, but we still do. One reason supermarkets have become so popular is that they provide perfect sites for scavenging. In the old-style grocery store the shop assistant did all the searching (she was a real scavenger, spending all her time working to find food), but in the supermarket we are allowed to search for ourselves. The

most satisfying and successful supermarkets are those in which
the bread is carefully concealed among piles of detergents and
plastic flowers. Any logical arrangement of the produce is
carefully avoided because it spoils the fun. If a manager is really
on his toes, he waits until the customers are beginning to find
their way directly to their foods, then he moves everything
around. The best supermarkets go even farther: they make it
difficult to get the food once it has been found. They pile the
cans of food up in terrifying pyramids so that the loose top
ones are out of reach. The customer has to prize one of the
lower cans out with as much care as a real scavenger once
needed to extricate a crab from its crevice. Pseudo-scavengers
enjoy all this so much that the markets are being forced to
install rest rooms and tea lounges to cater to customers who
stay there searching long after they have found what they
need. There is only one system better than the supermarket
for superomnivores and that is the original one of finding food
in the wild. A few people with really high search urges still do
this and go travelling long distances to spend days in some
forest collecting mushrooms that could have been bought at
the local market in a few minutes for a fraction of the cost. But
the cost, as we have seen, is unimportant. It is the successful
search that counts.

We are all pseudo-scavengers. Those who cannot search for
food compensate by giving the search urge new goals. They
go bird watching (it should really be called bird searching),
where the pleasure lies in finding the bird and looking for its
name in a book. They invent games, such as train spotting,
which are camouflaged with expertise and jargon, but are
obviously attractive simply because they involve a search
for something. People search in antique markets for glass
paperweights and first editions. Many intrinsically worthless
objects have acquired an artificial value as a result of competition between those whose search urges happen to coincide.
This gives the objects greater attraction and makes the search
even more enjoyable. Some pseudo-scavengers divert their
need to search into more sedentary channels. They search
for hidden words in anagrams and crossword puzzles. Most

newspapers publish a new area for word searching every day and offer no financial reward as an inducement to take part. There is no need to; the word scavengers find their own reward in finding the answers.

All these pseudo-scavenging activities involve a search for a definite kind of object. There must be a search image involved. It does not matter whether this is a steam locomotive or a six-letter word beginning with X. Both function in limiting the field and directing the search to a more or less specific goal. This is necessary because nobody enjoys random searching. There are few things more infuriating than forgetting what you are looking for. So the search is not a goal in itself. For satisfaction one must find something. And not just anything, but the thing contained in the search image. Our pseudo-scavenging searches can be directed towards all sorts of strange goals. But, where food itself is concerned, modern man's search images are still very much influenced by his inheritance.

As true scavengers, we went looking for a wide variety of foods. These had certain characteristics in common which helped protomen find and recognise them and which still determine our choice of food today. Colour is one of the most obvious. Ripe fruits are usually some shade of red or orange, roots and shoots are yellowish, nuts and edible animals are most often brown. All these are warm colours that would have been distinctive against the green of foliage or grass. We still seek them out and tend to avoid the cold colours. We have a deep-seated dislike for blue foods. Take a trip through a supermarket and see how many blue ones you can find. They are rare in nature and equally rare in our artificial hunting grounds. No sweet manufacturer ever successfully marketed a blue confection, and no blue soft drink or ice cream appeared on sale for very long. The wrappers on foodstuffs are seldom blue for the same reason, but we do use blue a great deal on non-edible products. Turn away from the frozen foods with their red and yellow wrappers and look at the shelves where the detergents are kept. A riot of bright blues and a very good clue that tells even a pseudo-scavenger that here is something inedible. Green is also a cold colour, but we tolerate it because plant matter is so often green and there was a time when we lived partly on leaves. Today we still eat a few, and when we do, we insist that they should be as green as possible. Food manufacturers oblige us by dyeing them. We obviously use colour as a key factor in the identification of food. It is so clearly the bounden duty of all oranges to be orange that the varieties that ripen when still green seldom sell well. Green limes, on the other hand, sell splendidly because we respond to the sign stimulus of lime-green.

Pattern is a factor closely associated with colour. Food objects that have broken disruptive patterns are likely to be rotten or even poisonous. Bad-tasting insect larvae, poisonous shells and smelly skunks all carry warning colours in broken patterns. Scavengers and predators learn to recognise these and to avoid them. We still tend to do so today. Pseudo-scavengers meticulously sort through fruits and other foods to find ones without a blemish. They usually head straight for the steaks that have a rich even pattern of lean meat and find it hard to accept that the best ones are those marbled with streaks of fat. The most attractive foods are the plain ones, and the most successful wrappers are those that are transparent and let this lack of pattern be seen. If the wrapper is opaque, it tends to have a plain pattern in deference to our tastes.

Shape and texture are two factors which vary considerably among natural foods. A complete range, from the smooth unbroken shape of an egg to the sharp very broken outline of a crayfish, is found in the wild. Real and pseudo-scavengers have a similarly flexible response to these stimuli. The only preference they show is for natural shapes and textures. In those countries where tomato sauce is served with a meal, it most often comes out of a smooth red plastic container that is shaped just like a tomato.

Size is an important factor in food choice. For a hardworking scavenger, it is a case of the bigger, the better. If colour and shape and pattern are all equal, most feeders will choose the larger of two food objects. Food manufacturers trade on this tendency by artificially magnifying size so that objects present a supernormal stimulus. This produces a supernormal response – people buy more. The process began with breeding fowls that laid larger eggs and trees that grew bigger fruits, but it has been extended into artificial packaging. Everything now comes in large, super, family and king-size packets.

Smell undoubtedly plays a part in determining man's food preferences. It is a clue which often helps us find food before we can even see it. The smells protoman followed most enthusiastically were those of ripe fruit and fresh meat and mushrooms. These are rather difficult to describe, but they are obviously distinct from the smells of overripe fruit, decaying meat and rotten fungi. Today we distinguish between them as good and bad smells and tend to avoid the latter. It was not always so. Early man often ate the very smelly stomach contents of freshly killed animals. Maoris packed grain into fern-lined pits until it decomposed and stank. Eskimos ate rotten fish, the Chinese rotten eggs, and one of the most popular fruits in Malaysia is still the durian which smells like a sewer. Today there is a return to foods of this kind by very sophisticated feeders. Cheeses with a positively faecal smell are popular in Scandinavia. It seems that smell, unlike the other factors which influence our choice of food, is more dependent upon learning and cultural influences than on biological inheritance.

We were scavengers for a long time (perhaps as much as 10,000,000 years), so it is not surprising that we should still be feeling the effects. About 3,000,000 years ago, we turned instead to hunting, and this has left us with an even larger legacy.

Food finding for carnivores – even those who live mainly on one kind of food – is a complex concern. All herbivores or insectivores have to do is find their food. Carnivores then have to go on and chase and catch and kill it. The whole pattern is longer and more difficult to learn. Some parts of it are innate, but inherited and learned components have to be specially arranged in an orderly sequence that ends with the death of the prey. Young carnivores play at hunting all the time, practising the sequence over and over again, putting all the pieces together into the right order until they can do it almost without thinking.

First comes prey location for which all carnivores have developed a delicate set of sense organs. Acute hearing is enhanced by directional antennae – ears which twist and turn to pick up the slightest sound of movement. Their sense of smell is so sophisticated that they live in a dimension we know practically nothing about. It has been estimated that a dog can detect the smell of one puff of cigarette smoke in a room large enough to berth a luxury liner – and probably identify the person who smoked it. In addition, most carnivores have superb eyesight. They are not able to see colours, but they are incredibly responsive to the smallest movement.

A hungry carnivore which sets out to find food does not wander about in an aimless way, waiting for one of these senses to be stimulated. It starts out with a specific appetite for meat of a special kind, or one of several special kinds. And it carries in its brain a search image – which is a compound of the various characteristics or sign stimuli of the prey. This compound idea is built up both by inherited instinct and by past experience of that prey. It is much more complex than the more generalised image used by a scavenger. An example of such a search image in our daily lives is the idea we build up in our minds when we are looking for an object that has been lost. Say, for example, that we have lost a golf ball in the grass. As we hunt, we carry a picture of the golf ball as a search image in our minds. The image may be a complete picture of the ball with its dimples and the maker's name and number, but more often it is an abstraction of the ball's appearance and all we are thinking of is smallness, roundness and whiteness. The result is that we will respond to anything small, round and white, like a mushroom or a pebble, and examine it a little more closely before deciding that it is not a golf ball. But, with this specific search image firmly fixed in mind, we will quite probably overlook something completely different, like a large angular brown pistol. And we may easily look right through the golf ball which has become splattered with mud because it too is brown and seems to have an irregular shape.

Nearly all carnivores have such a search image system. It can be very easily demonstrated by giving a mongoose a rough porcelain dummy egg – so crude that it would probably not fool a fowl. All mongooses will carry the egg around and try to break it – in spite of the fact that it does not feel or sound or smell anything like an egg. Their search image for eggs is made up of only the egg shape. This is all they need to look for because, in the wild, there are unlikely to be any confusing porcelain eggs lying around. The real value of a search image to a predator is that it enables him to recognise his prey instantly and even to pick it out of a confusing barrage of other stimuli. Recognising it instantly, he can instantly respond to it – and perhaps launch an attack before it is aware of his presence.

The attack is the second stage of the hunting sequence which ends with the final kill. All the stages leading up to this consummatory act are known as appetitive behaviours. The first is the period of undirected searching behaviour in which the predator covers the areas where his prey is most likely to be found. As soon as one of the senses picks up a stimulus which corresponds to the search image the predator's behaviour changes from first-stage random searching to second-stage directed stalking of a specific prey object. The actual method of stalking depends on the species concerned.

There is a great deal of variety in the methods and in the choice of weapons. Most of the carnivores have long, sharp canine teeth. The highly efficient cats have sheathed claws to add to their armament. Bears, which kill only occasionally, do so with a cuff from a hefty paw. In a sense, all body adaptations which have arisen to make a predator more efficient are weapons. These include the slim body of the weasel, the webbed feet of the otter, the whiskers of the cats and the big brain of man.

The weapons are turned on the prey to kill it. This is the final act in the sequence. Originally eating was the last stage that left an animal satiated and no longer feeling the need to go out hunting. But killing is such a powerful piece of behaviour – one which has become so fundamental to a carnivorous life – that the act has become a goal in itself. A goal so important that if the animal has eaten (even to repletion) without killing, its urge to hunt will still be unsatisfied. This often happens to domestic cats and dogs, which receive all their food ready-killed. They are no longer hungry, but they still need to kill and usually have to take this urge out on balls of wool or slippers.

Man relinquished his role as a killer and hunter when he became a settled farmer about 10,000 years ago. He became domesticated and well fed, but he still needed to hunt. He found his equivalent of the ball of wool in working and playing. In a million years of hunting, man formed close ties with other adult males in the tribe and grew used to a life involving constant risks and challenges. So he turned work into an activity that involved him, with other men, in a recurring gamble that has many characteristics of the hunt. To take an example drawn from only one kind of work, he set aside hunting grounds (business centres) where the prey (his rivals) could be stalked (with the aid of industrial espionage) and captured (in a take-over bid). In the all-male gatherings that have always followed the hunt, the money hunter is able to boast of his prowess and of the 'killing' he has just made. Other kinds of work make less effective substitutes for hunting, and the workers are forced into pseudo-hunting activities of a different kind. We will discuss these later, but one further point is worth making here.

Only the men were involved in hunting. The women stayed at the home base and continued to scavenge while rearing their young. When man switched from hunting to farming and other kinds of work, the women were given a more secure and better organised home base, but their way of life did not change a great deal. This change had to wait until labour-saving and contraceptive devices made it possible for women to choose another way of life. Many have, but they are finding that it is not easy and that the human animal cannot just discard a million years of evolution. Man needed a substitute for hunting and now women are finding that they need a substitute for maternity. A few women, as spinsters always have, find substitute families of schoolchildren or junior nurses or cats. Others go into the male world of pseudo-hunting but seldom find it a completely satisfactory solution. There is a rapidly growing sense of unease among women who are left in this behavioural limbo. Men channelled the hunting skills of strategy and ruthlessness into pseudo-hunting. Women will have to find a similar outlet for the skills they acquired in maternity.

The human mother needs a strong protective response and an ability to take great pains with the slow step-by-step training of someone who is dependent on her for many years. This sounds like the description of a perfect secretary. Women do make better secretaries than men, but pseudo-maternity need not be merely an adjunct of pseudo-hunting. I have this vision of a vast army of pseudo-mothers (whose potential membership is already about one billion) taking on the whole human species as a child substitute. Organising themselves into squads of super-administrators and painstakingly supervising the emergence of a completely new social order. The type of system that many men have dreamed of, but none have had the patience or the skill to put into practice.

To return once more to pseudo-hunting, there are other ways in which it can manifest itself. One of these is in play. The young of predatory animals practise hunting and killing in their games. It is no accident that the word 'game' is itself also used to describe animals which are hunted. In our species, children (usually boys – the apprentice hunters) play any number of games that include a chase. In some of these, one of the players takes the part of the prey. But in many games a ball is used as a prey substitute. In some cases the ball even has feathers attached to it and is called a bird. There is an Argentine horseback game that is now played with a ball that has handles, but the original ball was a dead duck. The Kazakhs on the Russian steppes play a game called *kop karri* in which the ball is a sheep's pelt. Many modern balls are made of pigskin.

Sometimes the ball is hit or kicked to give it life, but often a player picks it up and runs with it. When he has the ball, he is the prey. When he is captured or brought down by a pack of players, the ball is said to be dead. Human children have always played games of this kind. When they were old enough to join the men in a real chase, they stopped play-hunting. But when man was deprived of his hunting role, he kept on playing the children's games. He made them more difficult and took them more seriously, but they were still basically the same games with a chase after a substitute prey. The games were also made more interesting by having several kills take place. After each kill or score the game was stopped and the chase began all over again. The victors (or successful hunters) in many traditional games were awarded a real prey animal. The prize for the Calcio in Livrea football match, which still takes place in a Florentine piazza, is a white calf. It is most revealing to compare the photographs taken of successful sportsmen and hunters. The poses are identical, only the prizes differ. But both silver cup and silver marlin are known as trophies.

Today the games have mushroomed into a major industry. They play such a major part in so many people's lives that they cannot be dismissed just as recreation. They are in fact a re-creation of something that once played an equally large part in our lives – the hunt. A large number of people do their pseudo-hunting by proxy, as spectators. Most of these are men – few women can understand what all the fuss is about. But, then, they never took part in the hunt. The men who most often play or watch these games are ones whose work is so dull and undemanding that it cannot serve as an adequate substitute for hunting. There are games like gymnastics and rowing that have had entirely different origins, and some of the chase games have been confused by the introduction of competing teams of hunters. But most of them still follow the old pattern of catch and kill that we learned as beasts of prey.

Some games like archery and clay-pigeon shooting are much more like the original hunt, but there are a few adult humans whose hunting drives are so high that they can get no satisfaction from a substitute prey. A few enjoy the killing games of fox hunting and bullfighting, but most go out after living prey with a gun. The fact that they persist in calling their prey big 'game' shows that even they are really pseudo-hunters. They prolong the chase and the pleasure by various self-imposed handicaps that make killing more difficult than it need be with the sophisticated weapons at their disposal. Some modern hunters eat their prey, but very few of them need to. Their need is to kill because man and all other successful predators have killing urges which are independent of the need to eat. The two systems have been completely separated and must be separately satisfied.

Wild cats held captive in zoos are given dead meat. Their hunger is catered for, but not their need to kill. Many species compensate for this by 'revitalising' their food – they throw it into the air so that it can be pounced on and 'killed'. Man does similar things. By the time a modern hunter sees his prey it is already dead and has been cooked and served up to him at table. So what does he do? He picks up a weapon and 'kills' it. Every week the senior hunter in every Western family commits ritual murder on the Sunday joint with a knife that is far larger than any carving knife needs to be. But it is more than just a carving knife, it is a stylised weapon that can only be wielded by the hunter. The woman of the house is permitted to serve the vegetables – that is, after all, her function as a scavenger. But by tradition, which recognises the predatory nature of the act, the man must do the carving. Sometimes strength is added to the illusion by 'revitalising' the prey. The animal's head may be left on to give it more semblance of life, or it may actually be served with a food object, such as an apple, in its mouth – as though it were surprised in the act of feeding.

Real killing in ritual circumstances occurs only when the food is not meant to be eaten – at least not by man. Sacrifices to gods always involve a prey animal. Nobody makes an offering by burning down an acre of wheat or by felling a fruit tree. When early man planned his first sacrifice, he included the object that meant most to him – his prey. And he delivered it in the way he knew best – by killing. As religions became more complex, the offering was made at an altar or high place. Later this structure was adopted as a dining table. Christians still refer to their altar as 'the table of our Lord'. This identification of worship with hunting and eating is not surprising for a species that owes its success largely to the lessons learned in the hunt.

But there were other lessons. Man, the supercarnivore, was not a specialist meat eater. He was still exploratory enough to take advantage of whatever came his way. Even as a carnivore, his interests were as wide as most omnivores'. His enthusiasm for meat led him to follow the large herds of game, and as he travelled, he learned. Modern omnivores like pigs and bears also travel widely. They have fairly well-defined home ranges but no fixed home base. They bed down wherever they happen to find themselves at the end of a day's meandering. They use their environment in a haphazard way, establishing no firm territories which they are obliged to defend against intruders. They have no need of exaggerated displays to proclaim their ownership of an area, no cumbersome weapons of offence or defence, and they are under no obligation to restrict their wanderings to the area near home. Physically and mentally they travel light.

This was man's way too. His only piece of heavy equipment was his brain – and he used this all the time. His efficiency as a feeder gave him some leisure, and he began to make necklaces and carved images and to paint the walls of his caves with wonderful portraits of the animals he most liked to hunt. Climatic changes split him up into isolated communities, and each of these developed along slightly different lines. One in the north concentrated on reindeer, carving their antlers into barbed spears and spear-throwers and producing rock paintings of their prey in beautifully shaded polychrome pigments. Another in the Sahara had difficulty getting near prey in the open spaces and invented the bow and arrow. There are still paintings there which show them using it in great animation. A third community abandoned hunting altogether and lived on shellfish. On parts of the Scandinavian coast, one can see enormous mounds of empty shells 1,000 feet long and more than ten feet deep.

While all this was going on in Europe, a new revolution in feeding was taking place in the old cradles – in the Middle East and East Africa. This was a change without parallel in the animal world. Ten thousand years ago man settled down and began to produce his own food. He was changing from a food finder into a food maker and starting a whole new way of life.

Farming produced an immediate and rapid increase in the amount of food available. It meant that man could lead a more settled life in larger communities where there was a more rapid growth of knowledge. The changeover did not occur overnight or even within several generations. The evidence suggests that the first people to live a fairly settled life must still have relied upon hunting and fishing to supplement their diets. The labour involved in growing grass was seasonal and would have allowed time for continuing with hunting. It is even likely that cultivation, as with many people today, was the concern of the women and that the men carried on hunting all year round.

From simple beginnings, cultivation grew rapidly, and the first farmers spread out all over the warmer parts of the world. The arts and plants they had mastered spread by imitation and acquisition even more widely than they themselves could travel. The first crops of wheat and barley changed as they were subjected to the effects of different climates and of artificial selection. In the east, rice and millet were added to the crop; in the south, sorghum; and in the north, oats and rye. Later, beans, peas and lentils joined the list and then dates, vines and olives. Oil-producing plants such as rape and castor were grown to balance the loss of animal fats and flax to replace animal skins for clothing. Almost every plant species that we cultivate today was already pressed into service almost 8,000 years ago. We have, of course, improved both quality and yield, but we have made few new contributions to the old list.

While women were mastering their crops, men were slowly domesticating animals which they had formerly only hunted. First came the dog, and then, with its help, he went on to herd and capture the wild sheep and goats. These were attracted to the human settlements by the possibility of food in winter, and, having a fixed home base, man was able to rear the young animals he found. Pigs and cattle came next, captured in their attempts to raid his crops.

The first pioneer settlements that sprung up in the Middle East and Africa spread along the coasts of the Mediterranean and up the Danube into the lowlands of Germany. Five thousand years ago they reached the shores of the Atlantic and over-flowed into the British Isles, where the older residents still lived as hunters and fishers. The revolution in Europe was complete. But only now can we appreciate what it meant. At the time, agriculture must have seemed like little more than a good idea for taking the pain out of finding food. But it was an idea that changed more than man's eating habits. Hunting man was very dependent on his environment. His needs were simple and easily catered to, and his life revolved around a family unit and the wild animals which provided them with food, clothing and weapons. He was very much in tune with these few things in his life – a fact which emerges from paintings which attain a degree of skill in expressing form and movement that has seldom been surpassed. But – like the specialist animals – if his environment changed drastically, he suffered. He had no control over the world in which he lived.

Came the revolution and everything changed. Farming man planted as much as he wanted to eat and herded enough animals to provide for all his needs, regardless of the vagaries of the weather. He lived in a large community of which he and his family were only a small part. He was deprived of the harmony hunting man had with his world; but the farmers began mining operations and axe trading, they cleared the forests and de-veloped polished tools, built boats and sledge vehicles, and perfected spinning and weaving.

These explosive changes all took place within a couple of millennia, just 10,000 years ago. With them, the farmers were able to lay a firm foundation for the growth of later civilisations – and all because of an apparently simple change in the way they found their food.

There is really only one alternative to finding or growing food yourself. That is to let someone else do these things for you. We who play the game as amateurs pay others to do it for us. But there are some who get theirs for nothing. There is a piratical sea bird called the frigate which waits until some other bird, usually the aptly named booby, catches a fish. It then dive-bombs the fisher until it releases, or sometimes even regurgitates, its catch. This is an efficient way of getting food, but there is an even better method that involves no strong-arm tactics. All babies use it. They *persuade* others to bring food to them.

Young birds have specific patterns of gaping and fluffing their feathers and calling which induce their parents, and sometimes other adults, to feed them. This response is so firmly built into a bird's behaviour that a sparrow has been seen valiantly trying to fill the enormous gaping mouth of a carp in an ornamental pool. Adult mammals feed their young by suckling, and some of the young have developed a special facial expression that says 'Feed me.' Monkeys continue to use this pout face long after weaning for begging food from their mothers and from other members of the group. Adults use the expression to ask one another for anything desirable. If a chimp troop is foraging on the ground and one member finds an unusual object, even a brightly coloured stone, the others gather around and pout until they are given the chance to examine it too.

There are also human beggars, of course. They ask for money, but they are good enough biologists to dress it up as a request for food. Their pleas are usually for something to buy a cup of coffee or a piece of bread. We have a built-in tendency to respond to this approach. It is bound to be more successful than appeals for money to buy a drink or the train ticket home. Even the international relief organisations have to play the game this way. Their posters asking for money show a wide-eyed child with an empty food bowl even when they are trying to raise funds for tractors or a dam.

Our tendency to share food is one that we acquired partly as a result of the hunt. A million years ago ape-men learned to kill large prey animals, and only then did they find themselves in a position to offer anyone else a share. Scavengers cannot afford to be unselfish, but hunters were able to share their spoils with other hunters and to provide food for their families.

Prior to the hunt, the whole group moved around, foraging together over wide areas to which they felt no special attachment. But when the men went hunting, they went on their own and there had to be some prearranged place for meeting the group later. So a home base came into being, and the hunter brought food to this base to be shared among the women and children.

Sometimes there was a little left over, but this surplus was probably never big enough or regular enough to have much effect on the hunter or his tribe. It is difficult to keep meat for very long. But it was in one of these brief respites from 990,000 years of hunting that the hunter and his woman launched the revolution. They invented agriculture, and, all at once, they had a really big surplus of food on their hands. In the next chapter we will see how this changed their lives and how, in the 10,000 years since the first large store was made, it has affected every one of us.

FOUR

KEEPING FOOD

I know a man who collects phalluses. In every other respect he is perfectly normal. Living in a nice suburb with a wife and two children and commuting each day to his real-estate business in the city. But his house and garage and a special shed in the garden are filled to overflowing with a vast collection of phallic objects, both realistic and symbolic. There are Egyptian stone ones, African wooden ones, Polynesian painted ones and even a collection of marble organs that he claims were done by Michelangelo and chopped off sculptures in the Vatican when plaster fig leaves came into fashion. He is very proud of his collection and maintains that he is no different from people who collect vintage cars or matchbox labels. He is right. The objects of his interest are a little peculiar, but the urge to hoard things is one we all know well.

Our literature is full of collectors of various kinds, including animals, such as the celebrated jackdaw of Rheims and a long succession of thieving magpies. At one time or another, every one of us has given way to the urge to possess a large quantity of objects to which we attach a special value. Tastes differ a great deal. Scrooge wanted gold; the jackdaw liked anything that glittered. Wood rats in Mexico collect buttons and pill-boxes, while others in California show a preference for ladies' gloves. In Argentina piles of silver-handled bullwhips are found carefully arranged around the entrance to the burrows of a large moustached rodent called vizcacha.

The motivation for most collections of this kind is novelty. All are made by opportunist animals which find something new and interesting and take it home to examine at leisure. A philatelist may seem bent on collecting only familiar objects, but even he is involved in a search for novelty. Keeping one stamp of each kind and exchanging duplicates for something new. Misers, on the other hand, collect the same objects over and over again. The money hoarder's obsession with quantity is so pathological that it interferes with every other aspect of his life, but it is easy to understand. It is simply an exaggerated form of a very basic need – the need to provide security.

In the beginning, security meant having enough to eat. So the first object to be hoarded was food. The simplest way of hoarding food is to get fat. When winter approaches and the temperature starts to fall, many mammals develop fatty lumps all over their bodies. Others put on weight whenever food is plentiful, regardless of the time of year. The Bushmen of the Kalahari, the aborigines of Australia and the Veddas of Ceylon all store food on their bodies. Their physiology is designed so that they can grow large buttocks in times of plenty and draw on these reserves when times get bad. At the end of several weeks of fasting, the swellings are reduced from inside until they look like loose folds of skin. Then, when food once more becomes plentiful, the whole process begins again.

All these people live in dry areas where food shortages can occur at any time – so they always have to be prepared. The prairie marmot lives in a temperate area where food only becomes scarce in winter, so it puts on fat during the autumn. In both man and marmot the hoarding is accomplished by eating more than usual. This urge to overeat has been built into their physiology over a long period of time and is now automatic, but it first appeared as a result of hunger and insecurity in an individual. Over the years food and security have become so closely linked that any kind of insecurity (even that produced by lack of affection) can lead to overeating. Queen Victoria grew immensely fat after the death of her consort.

Getting fat, as we know, has its drawbacks. Many animals cannot afford to do it because it makes them heavier and less able to run from their predators. It would also make a predator less effective in running after its prey. When man first adopted this system of food storing, he was a predator. There must have been all sorts of unsuccessful experiments before the body finally hit on the idea of putting it on the buttocks where it would cause least inconvenience in running. The fact that, in this position, it also provided the greatest comfort in sitting clinched the arrangement. We still have small stores of fat on our bottoms. These are more developed in women partly because they were less involved in hunting and did not need to be able to run so fast. First-rate female athletes today have small masculine bottoms and very little padding on their hips.

Those animals which are unable to grow fat have to find some other solution. Simple animals just take the easy way out. If a lungfish is threatened by drought, it curls up in the mud. If a python has trouble finding food, it goes without for several months. For mammals it is not so easy. They have a much higher rate of metabolism and cannot afford to react passively to hostile changes in the environment. Warm-blooded mammals live several times as fast as their cold-blooded ancestors. This high-powered way of life has made it possible for them to colonise practically every habitat on earth, but it also makes it necessary for mammals to find new ways of overcoming old food shortages. Being basically opportunistic, they have come up with all sorts of new ways. To understand these, and to appreciate their effects on human behaviour, we have to compile a cache register – a survey of the species which hoard and an examination of their reasons for doing so.

When a number of animals feed together at the same site, they compete for the food. No food item is safe until it is actually in someone's mouth. To give themselves an advantage, some mammals have developed cheek pouches that can be loaded with a lot of food very quickly. By stuffing their faces full in a short space of time, they provide security not only for the food but also for themselves. Popular feeding places are dangerous because a large crowd of feeders attracts predators. For this reason, most animals are jumpy and reluctant to feed there. They try, if possible, to take food to a safe place before eating it.

Observations in school playgrounds show that a similar force is in action in man. These were made during recesses from school – during a short morning break when no food was consumed and a longer midday break when the pupils had access to their lunch packs. At both times the children split up into a number of groups. But during the feeding interval they were more dispersed, the average size of each group being only one-third as large as the average for the non-feeding interval. There are few predators for us to worry about today, but we still feel ill at ease when feeding in a crowd.

Cattle and deer have one solution to the problem. They rapidly swallow their food at the feeding site and later, in a place of greater safety, regurgitate it bit by bit and chew these cuds at their leisure. This is obviously an efficient system, so many feeders still use it. But it involves a physical specialisation that commits the feeder to eating grass forever. Some mammals are too opportunist to go this far, so, instead of altering their structure, they adapt their behaviour. They needed to eat in security; the place of greatest security was the home; so they took food home. It is only a short step from 'taking food home to eat' to 'taking home more than you can immediately eat'. And so true food hoarding began.

At first it was a deliberate decision. Later it became a built-in pattern of behaviour. There is a good human example of the sort of process involved. Certain Trobriand islanders live almost entirely on yams and would starve if anything happened to their annual crop. They have, however, a time-honoured tradition of storing each year's yams and living off those from the previous year. The tradition is enforced by the chief, who presides over a ceremony of food hoarding performed each year at the time of the harvest. It is doubtful if even he realises the significance of the ritual which is carried out year after year by a tribe who cannot remember a crop ever having failed. But if one should, they will owe their survival entirely to the tradition and the hoard. Food hoarding in other mammals began in just this way – as a tradition handed down by example. If one were to take a baby Trobriander away from his tribe, before he had seen or heard about the ceremony, and raise him in a community which did not have the same sort of ritual, it would play no part in his life. The pattern would be lost. To guard against this, hoarding mammals have managed – over millions of years – to make the pattern instinctive. Today a young hamster reared in complete isolation from other hamsters still fills its cheek pouches in exactly the same way as its parents and builds a pile of food in its nest without instruction of any kind. The species needs to hoard in order to survive, so each individual is programmed with the appropriate patterns.

The human position is rather different. Man and his ancestors survived for millions of years without hoarding food. Even now there is not one other primate which does it. Few of them have fixed home bases and all of them live in areas where hoarding is unnecessary. Our ancestors, however, were more ambitious. They moved out of the tropical forest into temperate and marginal areas where food was sometimes hard to find. Other animals in similar situations responded by laying in supplies of their favourite foods. Early man's response was to increase the range and quality of foods he favoured. He became omnivorous and joined the baboons and raccoons, which are quite unconcerned about local shortages. If there are no roots and shoots, they turn to bugs and grubs. And if this fails, they quickly turn to catching frogs and fish. When even these fail, they take advantage of the benefits of food hoarding – they dig out a burrow and eat both the hoarder and his hoard.

Early scavenging man lived in just this way. Some groups still do. The Congo Pygmies, the Andaman islanders and the Semang of Malaysia all enjoy a scavenging existence in which the hoard is unheard of. They either feast or fast, but they seldom have to go without for very long. There are times when game is plentiful, when fish are running, when plants are in season or fruits are ripe. They keep track of these events and make sure they are in the right places at the right times. This means being mobile and doing without a home or a hoard, but hunting and gathering men can survive without either. We might still be at this level of development if our ancestors had

not been so opportunist that, in spite of living fairly comfortably,
they had to explore every possibility. One that intrigued them
was the idea that they need not work so hard for a living. So
they began to collect more food than they could immediately
eat. There is no built-in mechanism for food hoarding in man,
so all man has to go on is the scavenger's tendency to collect
the things he likes.

The first human food hoarder was probably female. We know
that the females of many normally non-hoarding animals take
to collecting food when they are about to breed. Digger wasps
collect caterpillars, hunting wasps paralyse spiders, dung
beetles roll up balls of faeces – and they all lay their eggs in or
near these larders. Mammals suckle their young, but a hoard
can serve them equally well by providing food for the mother
during its confinement. There is a record of a female polecat
which paralysed forty frogs by biting them through the head
and stacked them neatly, together with eleven eels, in the den
where it gave birth to its young. And another of a female
weasel which built its nest around a store of forty-four mice
and a brace of magpies, all beautifully set out and separated
from each other by layers of sand. A human female would
find her normal scavenging activities considerably curtailed by
giving birth and having to rear a baby. She could offset this
disadvantage by accumulating some sort of surplus. So she
collected nuts and bulbs and became the first hoarding primate.

The advantage of coming to hoarding at such a late stage in
evolution is that man was able to adopt so many different kinds
of hoarding behaviour and to use them in so many ways.
One of the first benefits was an extension of his range. With a
store of food, even if it was only a small pack of iron rations
carried on his back, man was able to explore and colonise new
areas. Bird distribution has followed the same sort of pattern.
Their ability to fly makes it possible for birds to move into an
area when food is plentiful in summer and to migrate as soon
as winter begins. In a sense this gives them the best of both
worlds, but in fact they are unable to get a firm foothold in
either. It is the non-migratory species, such as crows and
shrikes, which occupy the greatest range of habitats and are

more intelligent and successful. They have been able to stay put in temperate areas and to avoid migration only because they store food. All of them bury food or push it into crevices or impale it on thorns. In the same way, it is not just coincidence that food-hoarding man is more successful than his non-hoarding relatives.

A hoard makes it possible for a species to be more widely distributed and for its individual members to be more sedentary. As humans spread out over the globe they set up a number of small communities. Each one tailored its needs to the demands of the immediate surroundings. Food finding was still a major enterprise for all of them. The size of this group was limited by the amount of food available. Sometimes they had to work quite hard for what they got, but these small surpluses in store gave them a certain amount of leisure. They used this time for painting and engraving, but there was not enough freedom for them to get down to improving their technology. Some of the living hunter-gatherers still go naked – even in the cold winds of Tierra del Fuego. Their homes are brush windbreaks or simple leaf huts, their tools are stone and bone, and their food is directly roasted over the coals of an open fire. They still live, as we once did, at this low level of cultural development because of an inability to accumulate a big enough hoard.

The biggest problem is preserving things. If you cannot store meat, there is no point in hunting or fishing for more than your immediate needs. So, when a large animal was captured, all hunting and gathering stopped until it had been eaten. Nothing was kept because leftovers just went bad. Only the Eskimos had an easy solution. They live on meat from caribou, fish, seal and polar bear. This is only available at certain times and then, especially if they catch a whale, in great abundance. But there is no limitation on their hunting activities because the climate is so cold that even the largest surplus can be kept. The Eskimos are food hoarders, and, unlike any other hunting people, they also have an elaborate technology. Sledges, igloos, tailored clothes, kayaks, needles, combs, jointed harpoons, lamps, pots, bags, buckets, knives and choppers have all been developed because they have had the time and the freedom that go with the possession of a large hoard of food.

Our ancestors had no arctic climate for deepfreezing their food, but they found an even better way of acquiring a surplus. They started a revolution. With cultivation and domestication came a steady and reliable source of food. The harvesting of crops once a year produced a large surplus that had to last until the following harvest. This meant building storehouses and silos and thinking more carefully about the problem. With thought came even larger surpluses and the chance to take some members of the community off food production altogether. They were given the freedom to develop their talents in other directions – such as pottery, building, weaving, trading – and thinking even harder. For a total omnivore with a food surplus, all things were possible.

One of the first consequences of the revolution was a sharp increase in the size of the human population. This was a direct result of the hoard. Today in Austria there are some wild brown mice which have only recently begun to build large communal food stores. These make it possible for the mice to lead a more social life. The result has been that their breeding rate is now twice as high as other mice of the same species which live nearby and have not yet learned to hoard. The total human population a million years ago was probably only two or three million. It remained fairly constant until about 10,000 years ago when the agricultural revolution introduced the first major change. After 3,000 years of farming, it shot up to over 100,000,000. Our population explosion was generated in the first large hoards of food.

These important stores were obviously accumulated in man's home base. We know that by the time he was a settled farmer he had a home in a territory that was defended by proper fortifications. The home and the hoard were housed together. It is difficult to decide which came first. A hoard of this size could only be built up when man had a home from which to work. But could he build the home without already having a small hoard to keep him going? The two things at this stage were interdependent. How did the relationship begin? Did hoarding first take place at a site that was considered as home, or did the site only become home once it had been used to hoard? If we look at other mammals for guidance, the latter seems to be more likely. Hamsters, for instance, will not defend a home site until they have made an attachment to it by building a hoard there. For them, home is not home without a hoard. The same is not necessarily true for man. It seems more likely, as I have already suggested, that the home base came into being as a rendezvous point and that food hoarding at that stage was quite unknown.

Whichever came first, it is certain that hoarding plays a large part in reinforcing a hoarder's concept of home and territory. The act of going out and bringing something in, if repeated often enough, sets up a distinction between what is 'mine' and 'not mine'. There are many people who do not feel at home until they have brought in a hoard of familiar objects and arranged them in a new house. Few cooks feel comfortable in a kitchen until they have stocked the larder with a vast collection of familiar spices – some of which they may never use at all.

This type of hoarding, which involves the accumulation of a single store in the home, is called *larder hoarding*. The first farmers were typical larder hoarders. So are three out of every four mammals which hoard. Hamsters, mice, gerbils and voles all make larders in their burrows. The ancestral rodents were burrowers, but recently a few have started spending more time in the open and some have even taken to the trees. These are opportunist species which are becoming independent of the burrow, but they still suffer food shortages and still need to hoard. What they do is to scatter it over a wide area, usually by burying one piece at a time just below the surface somewhere in their territories. This behaviour is called *scatter hoarding*. All squirrels are scatter hoarders. The classic notion of a squirrel making a big pile of nuts in a warm tree hollow is completely wrong. They never do it – not even to please us. Most carnivores which hoard do so in a scatter. Foxes and coyotes bury eggs and bones all over the place. The Bushmen scatter-hoard water by burying ostrich eggshells full of it at strategic points all over their hunting grounds. Modern man is a scatter hoarder, spreading his larders out over thousands of miles in chains of supermarkets or warehouses. Our communities are now so complicated that a Briton's bread may come from Canada and his butter from New Zealand, and both countries will hoard it until he needs it.

We have been able to create long-term and long-distance hoarding systems because we have discovered not only how to keep food but how to keep it fresh. The Eskimos have always preserved stores by freezing them, but they were not the first to make the discovery. The short-tailed shrew lives mainly on snails which it captures when they are immobile on cold days. It stores them in batches of about eighty in special underground chambers filled with damp, loose soil. In the coldest weather, when the temperature on the surface is very low, the shrew takes the snails out and piles them up like a deepfreeze selection outside the entrance to its burrow. Then, when it becomes warm outside, the snails are once again taken down to the cooler underground chamber and so kept permanently fresh and immobile. The European mole does something similar with earthworms which it collects when they are sluggish in the autumn and embeds in the cold earth walls of its tunnels by the hundred. To make perfectly sure that they do not escape, the mole bites off the first few segments of each worm, rendering them helpless until they have had time to repair the damage. Cold can keep food fresh indefinitely. Woolly mammoths have been kept fresh in the Siberian deep-freeze for 10,000 years. The meat of one excavated recently was served in several Moscow restaurants.

Modern refrigeration techniques began with the Romans, who brought cartloads of ice down from the Alps and packed it into their cellars. The practice later spread right across Europe. Francis Bacon died of pneumonia caught while gathering snow to stuff and preserve a chicken. Today we have equipment for producing much lower temperatures and for preserving food by accelerated freeze-drying.

Animals were drying food long before it occurred to man. Squirrels hang mushrooms out to dry on branches in the sun, where they keep for months. Kangaroo rats collect green seeds when these are available in spring and early summer. They would decay if taken at once to the underground stores where the soil is moist in summer. So the rats scatter-hoard the seeds by burying them in shallow surface pits until they have been dried by the sun. Only in late summer are the dry seeds transferred to underground larders. The early farmers discovered, perhaps by watching squirrels and shrikes, that meat and fish kept longer if hung out to dry in the sun. When the weather was bad, they perfected the technique of drying meat by smoking it above a fire.

We cannot even lay claim to the discovery of preservatives. The pine squirrel in California uses water. It puts pine cones into moist ground around the edges of pools, where they stay tightly closed and fresh for years. The cones open immediately on being exposed to dry air. The first farmers found that salt water worked equally well with meat and that sugar water would preserve fruit. One of them, probably by accident, discovered that fish cooked and kept in olive oil were preserved. Today we still keep sardines this way, but now the oil is isolated in an airtight can. The principle is an old one, dating back to the first farmer's wife who found that meat kept longer than usual if allowed to cool in a cooking pot with an unbroken layer of fat across the top. It was modernised only in the nineteenth century when Napoleon demanded that someone provide him with a way to keep food surpluses long enough to overcome shortages caused by the British blockade of his ports. A Parisian showed him how to seal food and cook it in an airtight metal container. It worked and the man was rewarded with money to build the first canning factory.

Perhaps the most surprising discovery in food preservation was that allowing things to go bad was sometimes good. Milk that goes sour produces a curd, and fruit juice that ferments forms yeast. With a little extra help, these products of decay can be turned into cheese and wine. Foods that not only keep well but actually improve with age.

Food hoarding, in all its many guises, has clearly been useful to man. He came to it late but used it often and to good effect.

For many animals it is a trick that is essential for survival. But for man it is just a trump card that can be brought out whenever he likes to give himself an even bigger advantage over the other players in the game. The hoard is so important to many feeders that they have evolved highly complex patterns to ensure that it is collected. One South American rodent – a sort of guinea pig on stilts called the acouchy – has developed a sequence of behaviour that is the longest, most completely formal, fixed-action pattern I have ever seen. The hoarding object is first investigated by turning it over in the front feet as the animal sits back on its haunches. It is then carried in the mouth while the acouchy looks for a hoarding site that has to be in soft soil near a conspicuous landmark, but not too near a previous hoarding site. At the chosen site, it digs the soil out like a dog, drops the object in, and refills the hole by alternately trampling downward with stiff limbs and sweeping soil in from the side with shovel-like movements. At the end, the acouchy places leaves and twigs over the spot to disguise it.

The whole sequence of finding, feeling, grasping, carrying, choosing, digging, dropping, trampling, sweeping, and covering always occurs in exactly this order. I have seen a baby acouchy do it when only six hours old. Everything is built in, nothing has to be learned, and hoarding can occur in no other way. Only one thing is variable: whether or not the animal begins the sequence. The level of hoarding varies from individual to individual and from day to day in the same individual. If the process were entirely automatic, then the level of hoarding would always be the same. Just as the number of hours an animal sleeps or the number of times it breathes each day is constant. But the tendency to hoard does vary, which shows that it is influenced by some other force. This force – which is the same for acouchies or hamsters or tigers or men – is insecurity.

The big cats do not look insecure, but tiger, puma, leopard and jaguar all hoard the remains of a kill by burying it under logs, stones and debris or by hanging it in a tree. They do this not so much to conceal the food as to conceal evidence of their own whereabouts. All four species cover fairly large territories, and it would be bad for them to advertise their exact position to their future prey. So they hide their kills from the noisy and conspicuous scavengers which usually warn prey animals that a killer is around. Hoarding therefore provides security for these secretive cats. The lion is the only big cat which moves freely among its intended victims when not hunting them. Its exact location is usually known. There is no need for secrecy and no record of a lion ever hoarding food in any way.

Leopard and puma sometimes come back to a concealed kill – so it also serves as a true food hoard. They find it easily, probably by a combination of memory and smell. There are other scatter hoarders which hide so many pieces of food that they cannot possibly remember exactly where they all are. Snoopy, of comic strip fame, claims to have total recall, but it is unlikely that any other animals do. Both fox and acouchy leave a scent mark on the hoarding site from a special gland in their front feet that secretes as they pack the earth back in. This smell persists and helps them find their way back even several weeks later. Each individual has its own particular smell, and this trademark also helps establish its ownership of the hoard and of the hoarding site. It is directly comparable to the human habit of writing one's name in each hoarded book or of putting a name plate on the home or office door. Not only do these 'signatures' tell others that this property belongs to us, but they also reinforce our concept of ownership and make us feel more secure.

The need for security appears in all hoarding behaviour. Chipmunks hoard rapidly when the temperature begins to fall. They do not hoard just anywhere, but in the comparative warmth and security of their nests. The greater the difference in temperature between the nest and the outside world, the more insecure they feel and the faster they hoard. I found that decrease in day length was also a factor causing restlessness and the need to hoard. Hamsters kept in a constant-temperature laboratory all year round still stepped up their hoarding behaviour when they noticed that the days were getting shorter. This is a built-in safety mechanism which prevents the animal from being fooled by the warmth of an

Indian summer. When I put the hamsters into a really artificial situation where neither temperature nor day length changed, they gave up hoarding altogether.

For the first farmers, autumn was harvest time – a period of intense activity as food stores were set aside for the approaching winter. Today we are no longer involved in these activities on the land, but shortening days and decreasing temperatures still spark off a time of feverish hoarding. We rationalise the tendency by calling it Christmas, but nobody knows the day or even the year in which Christ was born. The Western church simply took over the pagan festival of the unconquered sun – a feast that was held for thousands of years to mark the winter solstice and the return of longer days. It was a time of celebration preceded by months of hoarding and marked by an occasion when the farmers broke open a special part of their precious store and gave each other presents of food. The first Christmas presents were all foods. Stockings still contain traditional oranges and nuts. With increase in day length and temperature, the hoarding animals emerge from their burrows and clear out what remains of the winter hoard. We respond in a similar way by unhoarding as soon as it is warm enough to open the windows – we call it spring-cleaning.

For many small mammals, possession of the hoard is a very real form of security. Upland mice in Manitoba collect as much as ten kilograms of seed in their burrows each autumn. If this hoard is removed in winter, they die. Hamsters have an accurate idea of how much they need to hoard. If given access to unlimited supplies of food, they hoard just so much and then stop. I found that if I put this amount into their larders for them, they would not bother to do any hoarding for themselves. Security can even be measured in grams. For some species, quality is just as important. If mice have been collecting oats all autumn and suddenly discover a source of wheat, they begin hoarding all over again with renewed enthusiasm. It is obviously useful to have several kinds of food tucked away in the larder in case one of them goes bad. In California, dusky-footed wood rats eat more than fifty different plant foods in the course of a year – and hoard all of them. This has the additional benefit of

insulating the animals against sudden harmful changes in diet.
They can keep on eating little bits of each, regardless of what
happens to be in season at the moment. Man the miser is
interested only in quantity, man the connoisseur is concerned
with quality. But most human hoarders are concerned with
both factors: sorting out the best quality foods and collecting
great quantities of them.

There are some large animals which never hoard at all; we
must assume that they find their security in some other way.
Whales, dugongs and seals have no homes or territories and
cannot scatter-hoard underwater. Their security lies in size
and mobility and in their efficiency as feeders. The same applies
to elephants on land. Bats never hoard but find security in their
superefficient feeding specialities and in an ability to turn their
metabolisms off at night. Bears and pigs never hoard, though
they easily could. They live, as we once did, fairly comfortable
lives as opportunist omnivores. They could probably develop
in entirely new directions – and even grow to be a challenge
to our superiority – if they were to add food hoarding to their
already impressive repertoires of behaviour. Perhaps they will
someday.

Man did. He found that a surplus of food produced a surplus
of food finders – and that these in turn produced a surplus of
other things. The process goes on and on, with societies
becoming more complex all the time. Each society placed a
special value on one particular commodity. It may be yams or
cows or gold. Whatever it is, the success of a member of that
society is measured in terms of the amount he has managed
to hoard. The individual may think he is working towards the
goal of a bigger yam pile or a better bank balance, but in every
case he is governed by the same old motivation. The same
need that sent the first little rodent out to find a few extra
nuts. The need for security.

We say security for us means a home of our own or a piece
of fertile land or the freedom to go where we like. But in the
end it boils down to having enough to eat today and knowing
that we will eat again tomorrow. After World War II some of
the children from Dachau concentration camp were taken to

the monastery of Kloster-Indersdorf. There they continued to steal food from the tables long after they learned that plenty was available. They stored food under their pillows and in their pockets, even when their stomachs were filled to bursting. They probably still do.

Modern man still has his moments of insecurity – two-thirds of our species do not have enough to eat. The few who have food to spare build up a large local surplus and trade with others who have a surplus of a different kind. These exchanges should have the effect of distributing food more evenly among us all, but each year enormous quantities are destroyed or dumped into the sea. This practice may be politically defensible, but it makes biological nonsense. The habit of deliberately destroying hoards of food is one of the few ways in which man genuinely differs from the rest of the animal kingdom.

FIVE

PREPARING FOOD

Somewhere in Africa a vervet monkey sits in a wild fig tree. It reaches out its hand and plucks one of the ripe yellow fruits growing from the stem. It pops it into its mouth, chews once or twice, and swallows. It all looks very simple. In fact, it never is.

We have already seen that the monkey probably had to travel some distance and use any number of cues, both visual and olfactory, to find the tree. Once in it, it had to locate the ripest, sweetest fruits by colour and experience. It may have had to fend off challenges by other males in the troop for the right to sit near the fruits. Being a primate, it will not have thought of hoarding any of the fruit. But it will have had to decide whether to stuff some into its cheek pouches or whether the situation was safe enough to relax and just eat. And even when all this had been settled, there would still be things to exercise its intelligence. The ripe fruits are often covered with ants which cannot be eaten or with caterpillars which can. These have to be recognised and dealt with. Then the fruits themselves have to be twisted in a certain way to pick them – this requires dexterity and practice. And, once picked, the stalk and part of the tough skin have to be carefully peeled away. Even eating this prepared fruit is complicated by the need to chew in such a way that the pulp is swallowed but the seeds are not.

In the last two chapters we looked at the problems of finding food and storing it. Here we will examine all the things that can happen to a food, taken from the wild or from a store, before it is actually eaten.

The first feeders lived in the primeval soup. There was no need for them to prepare their food in any way; they simply absorbed it through their body surfaces. Later they and their needs became more complex. They learned to live off each other, and as predator and prey both developed, they discovered new problems. Their digestive surfaces were no longer in constant intimate contact with their food supply, so they were faced with the problem of getting the food outside, inside. This involved preparing it in some way. Definite patterns emerged for dealing with the foods most often eaten, and over millions of years these patterns became hereditary. Finally, even the instincts were found to be insufficient for proper food preparation and these were supplemented by all sorts of complex traditions.

The mammals, as usual, developed the most complex patterns of all. Before examining these, and their effect on our behaviour, we will take a quick look at the mechanics involved. At the built-in tools that mammals have to take hold of their food.

The first and most primitive instrument is the mouth. Today there are still many feeders which rely entirely on their teeth for grabbing food. All of them have fallen back on this simple solution because their limbs have become specialised for rapid movement, so they cannot be spared for feeding. One group of teeth feeders is preoccupied with running away from its predators and the other with swimming towards its prey. The runners are all herbivores, such as antelope and sheep. None of them ever uses a hoof even to hold a piece of food down while pulling at it with its teeth. The swimmers are all carnivores, such as whales and seals whose limbs have become paddles. None of these flippers is suitable for handling food, but the swimmers all have excellent brains, and we know that it has occurred to at least one of them to use a limb in this way.

A dolphin kept in a narrow glass-fronted tank in a research laboratory found the water too shallow for its liking. It registered its protest by stuffing a fish into the overflow pipe. The lab was flooded out, and the researchers, getting the message, began to build a larger tank. While this was under construction, they took steps to prevent further protest floods by removing all uneaten fish from the tank each evening. Despite this precaution, it happened again. The dolphin waited for the evening inspection, hid a fish in its mouth, and then used it as a plug as soon as everyone had gone. Thereafter, the evening round included a look inside the animal's mouth, but once more the building was inundated. Only round-the-clock observation by a hidden watcher showed how the dolphin did it. It ate all but one of its daily fish ration, saved this up in its mouth throughout the day, and when the time came for the oral checkup, tucked it under its flipper.

Some foods cannot be collected with the teeth alone, so a few mammals with teething troubles have used other parts of their faces to help them feed. Anteaters use long muscular tongues. Tapirs have grown protrusible lips which they wrap around food like a hand. Elephants have become so large that their weight must be supported by four huge feet firmly planted on the ground. But they needed a grasping instrument and came up with the unique idea of using an elongated nose. The tip of this trunk has been so beautifully modified with fingerlike projections that an elephant can untie a shoelace or pick up a paper clip. This type of manipulation by trunk has the splendid name of trombipulation.

There is only one other instrument capable of such fine precision handling and that is the hand itself. Particularly the five-fingered human hand with its fully opposable thumb. We tend to think of our hands, with all their delicate muscles and sophisticated movements, as very advanced. But they are in fact rather primitive. The first little insect-eating mammals had five digits on each foot. It was only later, as some became larger and faster runners, that they lost one or more of the fingers. You can demonstrate, with your own old-fashioned five fingers, just how this specialisation took place.

Lay your right hand palm downwards flat upon a table. This is the original flat-footed stance of the ancestral mammal. Bears

still use it today, shuffling around with the whole sole of the
foot in contact with the ground. Now lift your elbow up and
lean forward on the hand until the heel lifts off the table, leaving
only the fingers lying flat. This was the next step in evolution
for an animal which needed to be able to move a little faster.
We can see it on the hyena. You will notice that, in this position,
the thumb is no longer so firmly applied to the surface and has
a tendency to lift off. It was the first digit to be lost as mammals
went up onto their toes. The cats and many other carnivores
have only four digits on their hind feet. Lean farther forward
on your hand so that only the fingertips touch the table, and
you will find that the little finger is the next to be lost. Tapirs
have only three digits on their hind feet. Carry on rotating your
arm and the index finger lifts off – giving a limb supported on
only two digits. All cattle and deer walk on their third and
fourth fingers. Finally, the fourth finger comes away, leaving
the limb poised on only the very tip of the middle finger. Horses
have taken this development so far that they actually balance
only on a modified fingernail.

We can demonstrate all these changes because our hands
have not become specialised in this way. They still have the
primitive pattern. The one way in which we modified the old
flat-footed stance was by transferring all our weight onto the
hind limbs. We are the only mammals whose bodies can be
fully and continuously balanced on two legs, leaving the other
two free for manipulation.

A number of animals also use their hands, but their success
depends entirely on how much they rely on the forelimb as a
means of support. Raccoons and bears can rear up on their
hind legs, and they share with us the ability to rotate the
forelimb freely at the shoulder joint. No animal which rests
solidly on all four legs can turn its hand so that the palm faces
inwards and upwards. And only animals which can do this are
able to use their hands to clasp and grasp. The first objects to
be manipulated were foods, and the first animals to manipulate
them gained a big advantage over other feeders.

The greater their manipulative ability, the greater the number of foods they were able to tackle. Large rodents like the

capybara are confined to lying with their forelimbs resting on the food – and restricted to a fairly conservative diet. Foxes stand and press hands down on their food to hold it still. They can feed on a larger number of foods. Opossums scoop things into their mouths using one hand as a shovel – and they are even more omnivorous. But the most omnivorous animals are able to clasp their food in both hands or grasp it in only one. These all owe their manipulative ability to the fact that they live, or once lived, in the trees. Their hands all have thumbs – fingers which have become modified so that they act in opposition to the other four. Most of the primates have opposable thumbs which make their hands the best all-purpose instruments in the world.

There are a great many foods that need preparing in some way. Some plant foods come prepacked, and fruit and nut eaters must invent ways of dealing with the hard wrappings. Each individual has a slightly different technique. A squirrel opening a nut leaves a 'fingerprint' of tooth marks on the shell which is characteristic of that squirrel alone. An expert can go into a forest and tell just by looking at the shells which species has been feeding there – and how many individuals are involved. Good rangers keep tooth prints of all the animals in their area so that they can accurately chart each one's development and position. They find that young squirrels unversed in the art of nut opening make indiscriminate scrapings at a nut. But, with experience, they learn to follow the fibres in the shell and not to work against the grain. In this way the squirrel soon learns how best to apply the minimum effort for the maximum return. Techniques differ in that some individuals gnaw a piece out of the apex of the nut, some make furrows running up to meet at the apex, some circle the apex and lift out the lid, and some slice the nut completely and neatly in half.

A few mammals have developed other means of dealing with hard plant foods. The capuchin monkey, most advanced of the New World primates, uses a tool. When given a hard-shelled nut that it cannot crack with its teeth, the capuchin looks for a suitable stone or hard object and hammers at the nut with rapid overhand blows. This hammering is by no means random behaviour; it is very clearly directed towards getting the nut open and the food out. In the light of evidence of this kind, it seems more likely than ever that our ancestors were using tools long before they became men or even ape-men. The earliest manufactured tools we know of are about two and a half million years old. There must have been tool-using protomen as much as three or even four million years ago.

Some foods of animal origin also come packed in very hard protective casings. Capuchins open clams in the same way as they deal with nuts – with a hammer. The most inspired solution is that of the sea otter. It carefully selects a thin flat stone before it goes foraging and carries this along until it has located some clams. It then brings the clams to the surface, floats on its back with the stone resting on its chest, and breaks the clams open by striking them sharply with both hands against the portable anvil.

Eggs present a special problem. They can be either carefully pierced and sucked or just squashed. Mongooses do not have large enough mouths to bite an egg or bodies heavy enough to crack it. But eggs are an important part of their diet, so each species has developed a way to deal with the problem. The dwarf mongoose puts both hands under the egg and flicks it sideways at a hard surface, like a rock or tree. The grey mongoose shoots the egg out backwards between its legs like a ball-player. And the marsh mongoose picks the shell up between its hands, draws itself up to its full height, and hurls the egg straight down at the ground.

Small mammals like rats gnaw holes through eggshells, but this takes time and is best done in a place of safety. There are reports of rats moving hens' eggs by working as a team. One rat grips the egg between all four legs and lies on its back. Several others then drag it along like a sled by tugging on its tail. I have no way of verifying these accounts, but they could be true. Rats are highly opportunist, and if you think about it, there is no other way in which a rat could carry an egg.

Other animal foods require far more elaborate preparation. Many have to be skinned or plucked before being eaten, and these are very complex procedures. As with nut-opening techniques, most of the method used is instinctive. A young leopard confronted with a dead hare or pigeon for the first time soon begins to clean it. It may make an awful mess of its first attempt, but it has the general idea. Skill comes later, with experience. A good indication that most carnivores are born with the food-preparation pattern built in is the fact that many of them show a need to pluck or skin which is as powerful as their need to kill. I have seen an ocelot in a zoo which would not eat its featherless dead meat until it had gone around the enclosure plucking out mouthfuls of grass. Plucking, like killing, has become a goal in itself.

Another fairly common method of preparing food is to plunge it into water. Storks carry insects to water and shake them around in it before swallowing. Birds do not have salivary glands, and dipping food in this way may have a useful moistening function. Several mammals are also secret dunkers, but they have little or no need to moisten their food, and it is difficult to believe that they are doing it for reasons of personal hygiene. Foremost of the washers is the raccoon. For two centuries this masked bandit has enjoyed an unfounded reputation for cleanliness. Generations of Americans have been brought up to believe that the raccoon has the commendable habit of painstakingly washing every item of its food – and they have been exerted to greater heights of hygiene by its example.

Though I hate to spoil the story, I have discovered that it is completely untrue. It all goes back to the great taxonomist Carolus Linnaeus who set a trend by giving the raccoon the name *lotor*, which means 'washer'. Every textbook published since has perpetuated the myth. The raccoon does sometimes carry food to water but certainly not to wash it.

What happens is this: a captive raccoon which finds a piece of food picks it up and carries it around. If there is a source of water nearby it immerses the object and then completely lets go of it. It then holds its hands out palms downward, with the fingers splayed, and dabbles up and down in the water, like a piano player or a touch typist, until it finds the food again and eats it. Not all food is taken to the water. I found that animal foods are dunked more often than plant foods and aquatic animals, like crayfish, more often than terrestrial ones, like grasshoppers. I also discovered that foods made dirty by rubbing them in mud are not taken to the water more often than clean food. And, finally, that dry food is not dunked more often than wet food.

The raccoon is not therefore trying to wash its food or moisten it. What it is trying to do is to satisfy a basic need. Raccoons normally feed in two different ways: they either search through dry forest and meadow for fruit, nuts and insects, or they search along the wet banks of rivers for crayfish, clams and frogs. They have very powerful fixed patterns for both types of hunting and perform them in about equal proportions. In captivity, or kept away from rivers and lakes, they still get dry food but no longer have the chance to satisfy their need to catch food underwater. No matter how hard they search in their water dish or in puddles of rainwater, they never find anything. So the raccoon takes food to water, drops it in, 'loses' it and then 'finds' it again. This provides it with an outlet for an inborn pattern of behaviour which has been thwarted. The search for food in water is rewarded.

With the raccoon, as with the ocelot which plucked grass, part of the hunting and feeding sequence has become a goal in itself – one which is not rewarded by eating. When this happens, it is important that the animal should be able to reach its goal. If it cannot, the need builds up inside it like water in a dam until everything bursts and the animal behaves in a completely demented way. Raccoon washing, ocelot grass plucking and perhaps human smoking are all important safety valves which allow the individual to let off steam in a harmless way.

There is one example of an animal preparing food by genu- inely washing it. On some islands off the mainland of Japan live colonies of macaques, a kind of stump-tailed monkey. One of their main food items is a sweet potato which they dig up near the shore. Some fifteen years ago, a young male monkey found that its food was more pleasant if taken down to the sea and washed. Today the whole colony is doing it, but none of the groups on nearby islands has yet learned the trick. This is a real example of food cleansing and an excellent illustration of how a food habit begins. It started by accident and is now being fostered by tradition. Given enough time, it could even become instinctive.

Most of man's food habits are governed by tradition. The fact that our adult habits differ so widely shows that we do not have an instinctive tendency to prepare food in any single way. Every organic substance in the world has been eaten by someone, somewhere at some time. And, subject to the limits of technology at the time, most types of food preparation have been practised on it. All these methods have to be learned by experience or by example. Man has no built-in technique for dealing with nuts and feathers. There are some non-human examples of food preparation techniques that are almost as complex as our own.

Orangutans in Borneo collect the leaves of a plant that is poisonous if eaten fresh. They bury these in shallow pits, cover them over with soil, and leave them for several weeks. Under these conditions, the leaves ferment and the product of fermentation is an edible and highly stimulating mush, which the orangs seem to enjoy. This behaviour is not instinctive. It depends upon an unbroken tradition practised by this one small population of apes which has somehow discovered the secret of pit fermentation. This is a process still used by men all over the world to render poisonous plants safe to eat. We have always assumed that sophisticated methods of food preparation like this are comparatively recent developments – appearing only after man settled down to cultivation. But if orangs can make the discovery on their own, then we may well have used quite complex procedures of this kind long before we came to agriculture. Perhaps even in our foraging days five or six million years ago.

Even simple hunting people in South America know how to prepare manioc. There are archaeological records that show it was being eaten 4,000 years before Columbus. And this in spite of the fact that the roots contain hydrogen cyanide and have to be pulped, soaked in water for a day, and then squeezed dry before being eaten. Complex procedures of this kind can become instinctive, but in man they never do. We are equipped only with broad tendencies and a brain big enough to learn all the little things we need to know. Cooking is one of these.

At first all food, including meat, was eaten raw. No fruits or roots or grubs were cooked, except by accident, until man became a carnivore. Even after this development, he continued for a while to tear at the warm flesh with his teeth. He was a killer and enjoyed the feeling and the flavour of food at body heat. But dead bodies soon grow disturbingly cold, and it is far too much trouble to have to go and kill again. How to re-create the warmth of living prey? If a raccoon can re-create the conditions necessary for satisfying its need to hunt in water, then a man can find a way of warming up his food. He may have done it in exactly the same way – by taking it to water.

All the earliest human and near-human fossils have been found in the Great Rift Valley of East Africa. The valley lies along a line of weakness in the earth's crust, and its formation was accompanied by widespread volcanic activity. One result of this is that a large number of hot springs still erupt all along the valley floor. Boiling springs and geysers of steam break through the lava flows everywhere. The fossils are found most often in sediments of ash and volcanic debris that covered the old living sites along the edges of lakes, so we know that there was considerable volcanic activity at that time as well. There will certainly have been as many hot springs as there are in the valley today.

Animals now graze all around the geysers, so there is no reason to assume early man would have been afraid to come near. There is every reason to assume he would have been interested in the warmth they created. It would not have taken him long to associate this warmth with body warmth and to think of putting his food into it. A piece of meat dunked in the water for a few moments on the end of a stick emerges at more than body heat. A very satisfactory way of re-creating the feel and the flavour of fresh-killed prey. And it would not have taken him much longer to discover that meat left in the water for more than a few minutes came out in an even more interesting condition. With the old flavour intensified and a whole lot of new flavours added to it. This would have been very important to a feeder who came to meat eating with a demanding set of taste buds acquired in ages of eating subtle-flavoured fruits and nuts. Carnivores without this background bolt their food down almost without tasting it. But man savours every mouthful.

I have conducted a series of tests at one of the hot springs in the Great Rift Valley and found that it is a perfect way of cooking, even by our standards. An egg emerges soft-boiled after six minutes. A chicken leg is cooked to perfection in less than half an hour. And it has the bonus of an interesting flavour from the mineral salts in solution in the spring. The only tools I used were sticks to put things in and pull them out – and to avoid getting my bare feet burned by the steam. Early man could have done it in exactly the same way.

I believe he did. I think it highly likely that our ancestors cooked food long before they came to terms with fire. All animals are afraid of fire at first, and early man was no exception. It must have taken considerable courage and a very long time for him to steal part of a bush fire and to keep it going in his home. It is usually assumed that he did this for the sake of the warmth and the light and that cooking only came much later. But the climate in East Africa at that time was not cold. It is far more likely that he had other and stronger motives for collecting fire. One was that he already enjoyed cooked food, and, having made the association between body heat and water heat, he was easily able to extend this to fire heat. He might have tried taking hot water to his home in a braincase or a gourd and found that it, like his meat, quickly lost its heat. But fire could also be carried to the safety of the cave or overhang where he lived, and it kept its heat as long as it was fed. More than that, if he fed it, it fed him.

Palaeontologists and anthropologists have agreed that an animal which cooks its food must be human. They have searched for evidence of cooking and found that the caves of Peking man contain layers of charcoal with burned bone fragments. So he cooked, but on many other counts they have no hesitation in putting him into the genus *Homo*. The situation is more difficult with earlier fossils. Arguments have raged for thirty years over some of the South African ape-men. One of them has been found in association with burned bones and has even been given the specific name Prometheus – the one who stole fire from Olympus. Some feel that this qualifies him for inclusion in the human genus.

In East Africa there are more manlike fossils that are even older. One recently found together with stone tools is two and a half million years old. Some authorities are reluctant to consider him human because there is no evidence that he used fire. Perhaps he had no need to – and did his cooking in the hot springs. There may even have been hunters using the springs long before they got around to making stone tools. Should they not also be considered as human? Unfortunately geyser cooking leaves no tangible evidence like ash or charred bones, so we may never know whether it happened or not.

There is good reason for using cooking as a criterion that sets man apart from the other animals. There are carnivores which enjoy fresh-killed prey as much as we do – and some of them have the necessary mental equipment for making the association between artificial heat and body heat. But none of them has ever carried food to flame or hot water. There are bush fires and boiling springs in most parts of the world, but all of them are exclusively used by men. Because of the heat involved, cooking requires the use of some kind of tool, even just a stick to rake food out of the coals. To use a tool like this, hands are necessary and the best hands belong to the primates. But we are the only meat-eating primates, and we are the only killers who have hands. This unique combination of meat eating and manual dexterity made us men and turned us into cooks.

Most of the cooking in the world is done by women, but the best chefs in the most important positions are all men. This apparent contradiction makes sense at last when we know that the first cooking took place away from home and was done by the hunters – by the men.

The first home fire was taken from another fire somewhere else. It was a long time before man changed from fire collecting to fire producing. The Andaman islanders cook most of their food, but they have still not learned to kindle fire. They keep an eternal flame going in each village and carry hot coals with them when they travel. The first home cooks did things in just this way. Methods of producing fire by flints and by friction were developed some time later. At first, fires were made just anywhere near the home, but later fireplaces were constructed by lining hollows with suitable pieces of stone.

When the stones were hot, the fire was removed and meat wrapped in leaves was placed on the hearth. It was covered with stones and left to bake. These were the first ovens. Then came potboilers – hot stones that were dropped into water in a skin-lined hole. These were the first cooking utensils. So, long before the invention of pottery, man could boil, roast, grill, bake, and stew his food. No really fundamental changes in the practice of cooking have been made since that time.

The first pottery was made about 20,000 years ago, but it did not change man's eating habits very much. Even when the Bronze Age came to Europe about 4,000 years ago, cooking was still primitive and food thought of only as a necessity. But in the eastern Mediterranean, food was taking on a different shape. Cooking was becoming an art. The Persians, Assyrians and Egyptians changed eating into dining. Their meals were lavish in variety and prepared by a whole team of servant specialists. They took the rough cakes of unleavened dough and turned them into delicate pastry. They prepared beef and goose with milk and cheese and added spices to the brew. Theirs were the first real kitchens, with charcoal fires, foot bellows, metal cauldrons and cooking implements. Then came the Greeks and Romans who added greater refinements. Bread making became highly sophisticated and bakers were raised to the nobility. Poultry was specially bred for the table and luxuries were imported from all over the empire. Kitchens were complete food factories with hot running water and chimneys.

After the Romans there was a return to barbarism and easy eating. It was not until the Renaissance that cooking, along with the other arts, came into its own again. This time the revolution covered most of Europe, and eating became the chief pleasure for all wealthy people. The cooks of great households were important and respected figures commanding

high salaries and carrying a great wooden spoon as a mark of
rank. None were more sought after than the French cooks
trained in the kitchens of Henri II by his talented Medici wife.
These were the first chefs.

Science began to make an impact on food preparation by
replacing wood fuel with coal and, in the nineteenth century,
with coal gas. Then came artificial aids, such as the replacement
of yeast by baking powder. By the twentieth century electricity
brought labour-saving devices. Iron replaced copper and pew-
ter and was replaced by aluminium. Today with the aid of
electronics, we have made the first major change in food
preparation for 20,000 years. We have found a way to generate
heat directly inside the food instead of cooking it from the
outside – and we can do it in a fraction of a second. Slot
machines using microwaves can deliver hot food straight from
the freezer in just the time it takes for the coin to fall.

Cooking brings about several major changes in a food. It
swells starch grains in cereal or potato and changes their
consistency from a gritty suspension to a smooth paste. It
breaks down the hard cell walls of plant foods and makes them
more digestible. It works on proteins, coagulating the white of
egg and softening the fibre in meat. And it destroys parasites.
But, and this has had more effect on our behaviour than all the
other properties, it also changes the flavour. It makes food
more attractive and more varied. For an opportunist species,
anything that increases variety is worth pursuing entirely for
its own sake.

Cooking also brought us kitchens. Workshops which turned
out inventions like furnaces and ovens, pestles and mortars,
rotary grinders and presses. Kitchens were the first labora-
tories and cooks the first scientists and technicians.

All this happened because we came to meat eating with
already finely-tuned palates. We were not prepared to take our
meat neat, so we cooked it and mixed it with some ingredients
that no other animal ever considered as food. These were
spices. Strange aromatic substances with names like tansy,
marjoram, coriander, tarragon, cinnamon, sandix and fennel.
Names which excite the imagination as much as the spices

stimulate our senses. Both the names and the flavours satisfy our craving for things new and exciting. We sometimes crave salt, but this is a strictly physiological need, and we recognise the fact by giving salt a commonplace name.

Spices have no food value at all. Our bodies do not need them, but the extent to which they appealed to our minds can be measured by their effect on history. Columbus discovered America trying to find a short sea route to the pepper and cinnamon of India. Vasco da Gama, on the same mission, opened up southern Africa. For four centuries England, Holland, Portugal, Spain and France fought over the spice routes, building up overseas colonies and spawning trading companies which wielded incredible powers. The centre of world finance shifted from Paris to Amsterdam to London according to which company was the ascendant. The demand was almost insatiable until, in true omnivore fashion, man got bored with the idea and moved on to something new.

Today there are many new entirely synthetic foods. We can have steaks made of cotton wool, coffee made from coal, and ice cream made from sawdust. We may soon be presented with something that feels, looks, smells, and tastes like chicken but contains no nutrient of any kind. We may also be eating high-protein foods prepared in the same unlikely ways. Protein is already being extracted from petroleum, crude oil, grass, old rags, seaweed, sewage and feathers.

Biologically, man the feeder is in a unique position. The distribution and behaviour of all other feeders is dictated by their food. Ours once was too, but today we can shape local food supplies to meet our needs – or bring new foods in from other areas. And as preparers of foods, we have no peers. We use primate patterns for dealing with plant foods and predatory patterns for making the most of animal foods. And, at the same time, we demonstrate our omnivority by preparing both plant and animal foods in ways which our ancestors never dreamed possible.

Whichever way you look at the game, we win (five-fingered, unspecialised, tool-making, fire-using) hands down.

SIX

EATING

This is the climax of the game. The moment when one of the players scores, he eats. Without actual eating, no sequence of feeding movements is complete. The appetitive stages of killing, hoarding and plucking may become ends in themselves, but unless they lead sooner or later to actual eating, they are meaningless.

The exact method of eating depends on the animal's structure. And this, as we have seen, depends largely on the kind of food it most often eats. With mammals, this relationship between structure and function is most clearly seen in the teeth. In the early years of human palaeontology, all that was known of one of our Asian ancestors was a single molar tooth. From this meagre evidence one scientist built a picture of the man it once belonged to. He described not only the diet (which was obviously coarse) but the size and shape of the brow ridges on the skull, the height of the man and the way in which he walked. Later discoveries of more complete specimens proved his predictions to be correct in every detail.

Looking mammals in the mouth, we find that they can be broadly divided into two groups. Those that swallow their food whole and those that chew it first. Man is a chewer, so we need not be too concerned with the swallowers. They are all predators which have become extraordinarily specialised to help them swallow a particular kind of food. It is worth noting in passing that those which swallow large animals have adaptations of the teeth, while those which swallow small ones do so with the aid of some incredible tongues. The plankton-feeding whales have piston-like tongues that weigh as much as a fully grown elephant. And the ant-eating pangolin has a tongue so long that it has to be housed in a cartilage sheath reaching all the way back to the pelvis.

All the chewing mammals use their teeth. With these they variously cut, slash, shear, and grind their food. The original mammals were entirely insect-eating and had little need for fancy teeth. But they came equipped with forty-four divided up into four basic types that could easily be adapted to suit the diverse needs of their descendants. There were six pairs of sharp-edged cutting teeth, or incisors, two pairs of pointed, slashing canines, eight pairs of shearing premolars and six pairs of grinding molars. All the later eaters had to do was to accentuate that type of tooth which was best suited to dealing with their own kind of food.

Insect eaters like shrews still have forty-four teeth, but they are all small and similar and housed in one long continuous row. Simple carnivores, like weasels, have a similar arrangement, but the more advanced meat eaters have teeth better adapted for killing. Their canines are greatly lengthened into perfect stabbing weapons. One killer, the sabre-toothed tiger, took the development too far and paid for its excesses by becoming extinct. Meat is more easily digested than plant foods, so meat eaters tend to have small molar teeth. Cats have lost theirs altogether and cannot grind food at all. Premolars are usually reduced as well, but most carnivores retain the last one as part of a shearing flesh tooth in each jaw. These carnassial teeth pass each other in a slicing action, like the blades of a pair of scissors. Most specialist flesh feeders work their food around to the side of the mouth to be cut by the carnassials. Animals which have them cannot move their jaws from side to side or around in a circle as we do.

The plant eaters have a different arrangement. They need to grind their teeth to cut up food as small as possible – and all have well-developed molars. The arrangement of the remaining teeth depends on which plants they most often eat.

Rodents need to cut food before grinding it, so they have enormous incisors in the front of their mouths. Because they often use these for digging, the cutters have become widely separated from the grinders by a gap that can be closed off by drawing in the cheeks.

All other plant eaters feed mainly on abrasive grass. The wear on their grinding teeth is enormous. To counteract this, they have developed flat-topped molars bound together with cement into a solid rasping surface. Premolars and canines are usually lost. Incisors are still needed for cutting, but some of these are lost too. Cows have none in the upper jaw at all, using their tongues to pull grass down over the lower incisors.

Cattle, sheep and deer have special stomachs which send cuds back into the mouth for later grinding. They have ruminating jaws which are hinged to move from side to side, as well as up and down. Each species chews in a highly characteristic way. Red deer chew each mouthful thirty times before replacing it with another. Some cattle make seventy movements or more. In many species, the upper and lower jaws are not the same width, so only half the lower jaw can come into contact with the upper jaw at any one time. The cud has to be passed from side to side. Camels strictly alternate chewing – left, right, left, right, left, right. Most antelope chew for a while on each side – left, left, left, right, right, right. Some cattle entirely chew each cud on one side of the mouth and then change over to the other side with the next cud. All the members of any species chew in exactly the same way.

Theoretically, it would be possible for them to chew in any way they liked. But they do not, so the action must be controlled by a very strong instinct. This is valuable because it allows them to go on automatically with vital rumination while still keeping a careful lookout for danger. They can do it in the same way that we carry on breathing – entirely without thought. Many ruminants eat exactly the same foods, but each has a different way of dealing with it. This shows that it was important to have a fixed pattern – any pattern – so evolution picked on the first one to make itself available.

Modern men have their cuds too. One sees pseudo-ruminants everywhere slowly and methodically chewing gum. We have no fixed pattern for dealing with it, but each individual acquires his own chewing sequence which is just as distinctive as any used by a ruminant. This may serve exactly the same function of making the chewer more vigilant. It is fascinating that so many gum advertisements stress the makers' claim that their gum keeps us alert and helps us concentrate on tricky jobs.

Omnivores, as we might have expected, show no specialisation. They keep the old basic tooth pattern. Primates have lost the old long muzzle and, with it, a few teeth. The incisors have been reduced from six to four pairs and the premolars from eight to four pairs – leaving only thirty-two teeth. A few species have long sharp canines for defence, but in most even these are altered very little. The great apes have a dentition so much like our own that it was possible for a hoaxer to produce a false human ancestor – the infamous Piltdown fossil – from a chimp jawbone. The differences are small and a few fossil teeth are still in dispute. Pigs and bears have completely different origins from us and from each other. But because they eat in the same omnivorous way, their teeth have become remarkably like ours. The teeth of a fossil pig from Nebraska were once hailed as evidence of an early American man.

The small differences between the teeth of modern men, modern apes and both their fossil relatives give us a good idea of the eater's diet and his way of life. It is easy to tell modern man and ape apart. The ape has an almost rectangular jaw with larger canines at the corners. These could be seen as evidence of a carnivorous way of life. But the fact that they are much larger in the males suggests that canine teeth are more important to the ape for fighting than for feeding. A common threat posture in most apes includes opening the mouth and drawing back the lips to show these teeth to the greatest effect. Man's canine teeth became smaller as soon as he developed even more formidable hand-held weapons. An ape which needs to appease a rival covers its teeth, while a man actually bears his in a smile and spreads his hands instead to show they hold nothing dangerous.

Man's canine teeth resemble the apes' in that they have long roots and erupt late, but ours have developed a cutting edge and now function like incisors. They no longer occupy a corner position in the jaw but have been incorporated into a smooth semicircle of closely packed teeth. From these alone we can tell that modern man has a mixed and unspecialised diet and that his lack of weapons in the mouth means he has developed something better that can be wielded elsewhere. If it is so much better, we can predict that with this superior weapon and his catholic tastes, he will kill to get meat.

Fossil ape-man's teeth show many characters intermediate between modern man and ape. Their jaws were more rectangular than ours and the canines slightly larger. Their molars were heavy and flat. This is usually interpreted as evidence of a coarse vegetable diet, but it can equally well have been produced by cracking bones and chewing hide. The wear on the teeth of Eskimo women who soften all their leather by chewing on it is very similar.

Today there are meat-eating men (Eskimos), insect eaters (aborigines), and plant eaters (vegetarians). After a life of eating in one particular way, they show small visible differences in the teeth. There are also cultural differences caused by deliberate mutilation, by eating too much sugar, by chewing betel nut or by high concentrations of fluoride in the water. Added to this, there is a fairly wide variation brought about by individual differences in the shape of the skull and the mandible. But, by and large, all men are born with similar types of teeth.

As a species, man eats so many things that he cannot afford to adapt to any of them. He has instead the ability to invent tools and to let them do the adapting for him. Every time he picks up a new instrument, he becomes a different kind of animal with a different feeding speciality. Give him a spear and he is a killer; give him a scythe and he becomes a grazer; let him make a ladder and he becomes the tallest browser. But for most foods our hands are adequate. There are a few which are too hot to handle and for these we have invented cutlery.

Instruments have been used to prepare food for a long time. As soon as early man began to feed on large objects that needed dissecting, he used sharp stones and prepared flake edges. When he started cooking his food, he used a stick to scoop it from the water or the flames. From the stick, he fashioned a sharp-pointed spike to impale the meat, and from the spike came more complicated utensils. Knife, fork and spoon each have their own long histories. It was not until fairly recently that the three were brought together to form a set.

First to appear was the knife. This goes back to the first stone blade, but it was not until the fifteenth century that it was specifically adapted for the table. Even then, it was used in the same old way – just to cut or spear food. It had a sharp point for this purpose until 1699, when Louis XV, fearing assassination at table, forbade the cutlers to produce any more and made it an offence to carry a knife with a point. There have been fashions for engraved knives, knives with straight blades and curved blades, long handles or pistol butts. Today the trend is for simple designs, points are coming back, and new materials are replacing the traditional silver. The change is due in part to the fact that cutlery is no longer a luxury – and one is not expected to take along one's own set of elaborately wrought instruments to every dinner engagement.

The fork goes back a long way too. It found its way to the table during the Renaissance, but as early as the eleventh century a Byzantine princess caused comment by using a fork during a visit to Venice. The practice spread to northern Europe only when ruffs became fashionable – it helped keep them clean. Even in the seventeenth century, forks were only being used for hot food. A hot lunch in France is sometimes still *déjeuner à la fourchette*. The oldest forks had two prongs, in the eighteenth century three became fashionable, and in Victorian times four were more common. Today, as with knives, the trend is once again towards simplicity and the return of three- and two-pronged styles.

Spoons are very old. The first ones were made from horn and bone by shaving them to a flat ladle shape. The bowl is the working end, and through the ages its shape has been determined according to whether the tip or the side was applied to the mouth. The shape of the handle also reveals customs and table manners. Plump handles, popular during the Middle Ages, were grasped by the whole hand. Our flattened handles are held in the fingers. When handles were thick, the bowl was easily fixed to them by some device such as a pair of ravenous animal jaws biting onto it. Later, with thin handles, the root had to be strengthened by a reinforcement known as a rattail along the bottom of the bowl. Today spoons are cast in one piece, but the rattail persists as a traditional decoration.

Even where spoons and knives are not used for eating, they are used in cooking. In the Orient, chopsticks take the place of the fork. They provide an extension of the thumb and forefinger of one hand, still allowing delicate manipulation but avoiding messy contact with the food. Chopsticks have been used for thousands of years and are unlikely to be replaced by Western cutlery as long as people in the East eat without tables. The food bowl must be held, and when only one hand is free for eating, chopsticks are far more efficient than forks. But we could see a reversal of habits. Many Japanese are today sitting down to table with a knife and fork, while it is becoming more fashionable for wealthy Occidentals to leave the formal dining table. They are beginning to eat in the living area, usually with one hand from a plate held in the lap, and often with chopsticks.

There is only one well-recorded instance of a mammal in the wild using an eating implement. Groups of chimpanzees wait until the termite hills in their area open up passages to the exterior. The termites do this several times a year when one caste in the colony has developed wings and is preparing to fly off and set up a new subcolony. When this happens, the chimps carefully choose a suitable grass stalk or length of vine and push it into the hole in the hill. When the stick is withdrawn, it is covered with termites hanging on by their mandibles. The chimps support one end of the implement on the back of their free wrist and pick the termites off with their lips. Like seventeenth-century dinner guests, the chimps often carry their own implements to a meal. One male chimp under observation carried a grass stalk for half a mile, visiting six termite hills on the way. This ability may be one common to all chimps and may have some basis in heredity. It is certainly very easy to train a captive chimp to eat with the aid of a spoon. Wild gorillas and orangs have never been seen to use an implement in this way, and they take far less kindly to it in captivity.

The termite-eating chimps use either hand for manipulating their tool. Like most other animals, they are ambidextrous. Many individuals however show a consistent tendency to use one hand more often than the other. In studying acouchies I found that sixty per cent of the animals used their right hands more often than the left and that all the offspring from two right-handed parents were similarly biased. The preponderance of right-handed humans shows that the tendency in man is also controlled by a dominant gene. Left-handed couples can only produce left-handed children.

The majority of our ancestors were also right-handed. Most of the stone tools could have been produced only by right-handed workmen. In one of the South African ape-man deposits are a number of baboon skulls that show similar fractures. All have been broken in by a blunt weapon on the left-hand side. Assuming that ape-man and baboon faced each other at the moment of the kill, such a blow could have been struck only by a weapon wielded in the man's right hand.

Until fairly recently, left-handed people were widely persecuted. Children were forced to write (even the word itself is loaded) with their right hands, and many naturally left-handed students were left only with stutters and psychological disturbances. Today we are more realistic, but every dining table everywhere is still set for right-handed people. The knife is placed on the right-hand side because it was the first and most important instrument and was usually wielded in this hand. When two-handed eating came into fashion, the fork had to take second place on the left. It stayed there, even though our eating styles have changed. It used to be socially acceptable to eat off the knife, but in the last two hundred years it has become taboo and most of the burden of the meal is taken by the fork in the left (for most people the wrong) hand. Americans have rationalised this situation by using the knife only when it is needed for cutting, then putting it down and transferring the fork to the right hand. Left-handed eaters, comfortable for once, just keep the fork where it is. When only one implement (such as a spoon) is being used, it is held in the strongest hand. But it is still set out on the table in a position convenient only for a righteous eater.

Most zoos today have published feeding times. These reflect the natural feeding habits of the animals. Nowhere will you see the feeding time of a mole or any of the grass eaters advertised. These animals eat all the time. Meat eaters however eat only occasionally and then usually at a certain time of day. The omnivores eat more or less often, according to the amount of meat in their diets. Bears are usually on the prowl for items in their mixed diet, but when migrating salmon are available, they need to feed only once a day. The difference between continual and occasional feeders is one which animal trainers know well. If an animal feeds continually, it will always be searching for food, and finding it will always be a reward. In training continuous feeders, like horses and bears, it is vital to reward each animal for every single performance. Lions and tigers, on the other hand, are usually trained without food rewards because they have very little interest in snacks between meals.

Man is in an ambivalent position. As a fruit picker, he munched away all day on snacks. But as a hunter, he took to a cycle of fasting and feasting. Now, as an omnivore, he could go back to the old scattered feeding technique, but men have chosen not to. Most of us concentrate our eating periods into two or more meals each day. We set aside a special time for taking our food. We eat more often than the true carnivores and less often than the true herbivores. We are real omnivores, with a little of each in our makeup. The times we choose for eating are significant. As tree-living fruit pickers, we were strictly diurnal and fed actively most of the day. As ground-living hunters, we found that it paid to hunt a little earlier and a little later. The twilight times were particularly successful. Typical carnivores hunt and eat at these times and spend the heat of the day sleeping. Because we are also herbivorous, we have an additional meal in the middle of the day. Today, urban man has an artificial day that stretches well into the natural night.

He tends to eat the large carnivorous evening meal much later and to pander to his herbivore alter-eater by slipping in a fourth meal in the late afternoon. The strength of this side of our nature is evident in the disputes that arise over this jealously guarded tea break.

Also significant are the particular foods we choose to eat at these times. The dawn and dusk meals are of carnivorous origin, and we usually have a meat as the main course – bacon and kipper for breakfast and all kinds of meat and fish for supper. The midday and afternoon meals are herbivore ones and much more often have an emphasis on plant foods. We are of course omnivores and try out new things all the time, but a strange feature of our meals is that some are more omnivorous than others. We are quite content to accept bacon and eggs (or coffee and rolls) for breakfast every day – in fact we insist on it. But if the same supper menu shows up on two consecutive nights, we begin to grumble. And if it appears again on the third, we find it very hard to stomach.

The answer could be that breakfast is a carnivore meal and that meat-eating diets are typically monotonous. But this is only part of the answer because supper is also a meat meal and yet we will not tolerate monotony in it. The rest of the answer lies in the other difference between the two twilight meals – one is eaten before sleep and the other after it. Our waking each day is like starting again. In the course of the day we re-enact both our own development and that of the species. We start off hesitantly, establishing familiar territory, finding comfort in familiar sights and sounds and tastes. Later in the day we become properly opportunist and keen to explore new territory and sample new flavours. Only the very secure can cope with breakfast parties.

Animals eat not only at specified times but also in definite places. Safe places. Eating is a dangerous activity because it means relaxing vigilance to deal with the complex problems of food preparation and ingestion. For this reason, most animals eat in a state of tension. We have inherited this unease, and, like the other mammals, we try to alleviate the fear by seeking out special feeding places where we feel more secure. Caterers make a living out of feeding other people, and they know that there are two ways of cashing in on table tension. One is to make the feeders so insecure that they gobble down their food, pay their small fee, and leave in a hurry to make way for others. And the second way is to make the feeding site so secure that feeders are happy to stay there longer and pay a big fee for the privilege. Both methods depend on a good working knowledge of the factors that influence man's choice of a secure place for feeding. Some restaurateurs are very shrewd biologists.

Man's choice of an ideal eating place is governed by all his senses. The first to come into play is sight. We choose a restaurant that has subdued lighting. It is true that dim lights have come to be associated with higher prices and that some of us will therefore deliberately avoid them, but we are never as secure eating under bright lighting. The lighting needs to be not only dim but also reddish. Designers say that red colours indicate hospitality and flatter people's complexions. This is true, but we really choose it because it is most unlike daylight. Successful restaurants seldom have large windows. And fluorescent lamps, which simulate daylight too closely, are never as effective as the old-fashioned tungsten lamps or candles. What we need, and are looking for, is the light of a cave or safe refuge. We need to be able to see into it before entering – a completely curtained restaurant always arouses suspicion. But, once inside, we need to see without being seen. We hate to be watched while we are eating. The colour scheme should be subdued and warm. We find bright colours stimulating at other times, but they make us feel insecure while feeding. A wise manager chooses the colours of walls, fabric, upholstery, carpets, tablecloth, tableware, uniforms, light fittings, glassware, menus, pictures and flowers all with great care. One out-of-place colour can set a feeder on edge.

The distribution of the feeding points also needs careful thought. No one likes to eat at an exposed table. We want our backs to the wall. Many restaurants solve space problems by erecting high-walled booths which give everyone a wall to put his back to. This also allows tables to be placed close together without disturbing the feeders. We may not want to eat alone, but we feel insecure if forced to feed too close to strangers. Very often the sacrifice of a few tables in the centre to provide an open space will give handsome dividends in increased security for those around it.

Sound is important. All floors should be thickly carpeted to absorb noise and to muffle the footsteps of anyone coming in. A potential feeder could be put right off his food if his arrival were advertised by the sound of his approaching feet. He must be able to get both in and out of the feeding site without attracting attention. Music, if there is any, should be muted and never contain vocals. Heating should be maintained at seventy Fahrenheit all year round, and in cold weather a radiant source of heat – real or artificial – should be visible. No single feature makes us feel more secure than a fire – and if it can be used to prepare the food, so much the better. The sight and sound and smell of food being prepared helps tremendously.

All these qualities – dim red light, soothing tone, intimacy, lack of crowding, muffled sound, a fire burning, food smells and unaggressive service – contribute to security and allow us to eat at ease. They are all suggestive of the cave – the family den with rushes on the floor, lighted only by the fire in the entrance. The cave or cellar motif is easily the most popular one in restaurant decoration.

In the high-priced, take-your-time sort of restaurant, that is. The proprietor can make as much money by deliberately designing a feeding site that lacks all these qualities. He can put in bright-blue lights, clashing vivid colors, low-backed chairs at tables packed together, strident music, echoing uncarpeted floors, air-conditioned cold or uncomfortably humid heat, and enormous plate glass windows fronting on the street. This will produce such guaranteed insecurity that it will give him a very rapid turnover. The fact that clever restaurateurs recognise these basic biological needs and consciously manipulate them is proved by a chain of large self-service eating places catering to both types of clientele. They have installed plastic trays with soundproof pads in their luxury premises. And in their eat-and-run lower-priced places, despite the greater cost, they have provided metal trays which create a constant clatter and keep the feeders moving.

One of the most vital aspects of our mealtimes is the company we sit down with. Farmers say that a solitary pig never gets fat. The same is true of most mammals. An individual eats more if he is in the company of other feeders. I once had to remove a three-month-old wildebeest from its family group for treatment in a zoo hospital. It reacted to isolation by going off its food and not eating nearly enough to restore its health. The solution, I found, was for me to stand with the young animal near the food trough while it was eating. This simple action more than trebled its intake.

The degree to which feeding is promoted by other animals depends partly on their social relationship to the feeder. Domestic hens eat more if feeding with another hen higher in the pecking order. The same seems to be true of antelope, who continue feeding until the herd leader stops. When the food source is more concentrated, as it is for carnivores, the dominant animal may feed first and prevent the others from starting until it has eaten its fill. With us, it is common for the tribal chief or the head of the family to be served first and to begin eating before the others are allowed to start. At larger food gatherings and banquets, eating is clearly socially facilitated. We all eat far more than we ever would on our own.

In describing feeding, I have deliberately ignored the fate of the food once it has been swallowed. The process of digestion and assimilation has been studied in great detail by others. It need not concern us here. As long as it functions efficiently, it has little to do with an animal's behaviour. But not all of the food is absorbed into the body. Some of it is excreted and appears again in the open where it can once more be an important factor.

Excretion is by no means a simple physiological disposal of waste. It follows patterns of time and space as rigid as those of feeding and can function in marking out territory and intimidating intruders. There are two basic types of excreter. *General excreters* who spread their waste out over large unspecified areas. And *focal excreters* who deposit it in one or more special places. Deer and cattle do not have territories to defend, and most of them are general excreters. Their piles of droppings are found scattered over their feeding range, deposited wherever they happen to be at the time. Monkeys are also like this. They live in the trees and their faeces drop down and out of their lives. They are so uninterested in the products of excretion they may even lie on top of them. This is something a cat would never do. They, and most other carnivores, have developed special patterns to deal with their faeces. When it is impossible to leave the den to excrete, as it is for young cubs, the mother may get rid of the faeces by eating them. Some herbivores do this all the time. Rabbits produce two different kinds of pellet. Those excreted at night are soft and moist and are immediately eaten and sent through the digestive system again. Those produced during the day are hard and dry and are left in a growing pile in a specially chosen place. A few herbivores have territories, and one, the hippo, has a special flat tail which it fans while excreting to spread the faeces over impressive areas along the boundary of its private grazing grounds.

Tree-living preman was certainly a diffuse excreter like the living monkeys and apes. But when he became a carnivore and established a fixed home base, he had to begin thinking about keeping it clean. He had to become a focal excreter and deposit his faeces in a chosen place in private like the other carnivores, instead of in public like the primates. Today we still regard it as a very private piece of behaviour.

Under natural conditions an animal eats as much as it needs. Too-fat or too-thin individuals are rare in nature and usually a sign of some malfunction which soon leads to death. But animals in captivity and humans, in or out of captivity, often eat too much or too little. After a crowded day at a zoo which allows the public to feed the animals, many suffer or die from overeating. This never happens in the wild, even when there is a superabundance of food. In captivity it happens most often to opportunist species which are affected by the lack of variety in their enclosures and perform all sorts of antics to attract the attention of the public. Unfortunately, with the attention they get food and get fat. Humans in prison often put on weight for similar reasons.

When something is wrong with a captive animal's environment, the opposite can happen. It stops eating. This may be due to the lack of other animals of its own kind or to the presence of aggressive animals of other kinds. Or the animal may simply have been given the wrong food. Man also goes on protest fasts and hunger strikes when something is wrong with his environment. It impresses us far more to read of an Asian statesman going on a week-long fast than it would if he gave up talking or wearing clothes – even though those protests may involve considerably more hardship.

Food occupies a central position in our view of the world. And eating it is by no means as simple as it looks. This apparently straightforward pattern of behaviour conceals all sorts of unexpected complexities. As with finding food and preparing it, the act of actually eating can be dissected to show that it contains a little piece of every meal we have ever eaten. The old hungers are never far beneath the modern tabletop.

SEVEN

DRINKING

Our brains are eighty per cent water. That makes them even more liquid than blood. Every chemical reaction on which life is based takes place in water. The equation is very simple. No water equals no life.

Two-thirds of every mammal's weight is made up of water, and some of it is always being lost through excretion, through perspiration and through evaporation in the lungs. Every time we breathe, we lose a little water. On cold days you can even see it condense in the air. It is vital that we make good this loss and keep filling up the internal reservoir. For man, this usually means replacing about four pints a day. But, in desert conditions, it can be as much as three gallons.

Part of the water we need comes in food. Except for a few things like sugar, which contains only a trace, most foods have a high water content. In some, like lettuce, the water is obvious. But even apparently dry foods, such as bread, contain forty per cent water. For some species, the water in food is enough. Kangaroo rats never drink. They get all their liquid from seeds and small tubers dug up in the desert. When they do, on very rare occasions, come across a pool of water, they have no idea how to deal with it and frequently drown.

Most other species must drink – and learn not to drown. They find their liquid in rivers, waterholes, springs, wells, rainpools or as early morning dew. A few can even locate it some distance underground. Elephants dig deep holes in apparently dry riverbeds to expose hidden water – a service much appreciated by the rest of the community during a dry spell. It is possible, with long experience, that they come to have an elementary knowledge of geology. They always dig at the lowest point on the outside of a river curve or at the back of terraces raised slightly above a dry riverbed. Experiments with human water diviners show that we respond to the electromagnetic field set up by running water. There is no reason why animals should not be sensitive to the same stimulus. The curve of an antelope's horns or a pig's tusks may act as a perfect natural divining rod, guiding the animal both to water on the surface and to a source a little way underground. Antelope and pigs both dig for water with great success.

When preman left the trees, he wandered into the deserts and dry savanna where he found water only with great difficulty. Lacking the keen sense of smell used by his prey, he soon learned to let their noses work for him. He followed game trails and the flight of birds; he learned to respond to certain kinds of plant and to the movements of insects. One early method of getting at underground water is still practised by the Bushmen. They dig a narrow hole to arm's depth and then widen it into an underground chamber. This chamber is filled with dried grass, a thin reed tube is put with its bottom end in the centre, and the hole is filled again with soil. The Bushman sucks at the top end of the tube and creates a partial vacuum in the chamber. This draws water in from the surrounding soil to fill the chamber and be sucked up through the tube.

Having found water, some animals store it. As with food, there are two ways of doing this. One is inside the body – the camel's way. Contrary to popular belief, they do not store water in their humps but in their stomachs. In a camel's stomach are a number of pouches that can be filled with water and closed off from the chamber by special muscles. The water is released from the pouches only when the camel can find nothing to drink and its system is losing more than is coming in. It can drink as much as fifteen gallons at a time – and go for almost two weeks without drinking again.

Man stores water outside his body in cisterns, tanks and dams. Some animals may do the same thing. A laboratory experiment with rats showed that if they were thirsty, they hoarded little rolls of cotton wool soaked in water. We have no evidence that anything like this happens in the wild, but there may be a small rodent somewhere which soaks dry seed husks in a pool and hoards a supply of water in a similar fashion.

The actual drinking of water seems to be done with far less ceremony than eating food. There are no very complicated or deep-seated patterns involved. The most stubborn captive, refusing all food, will drink water with hardly any fuss. Because drinking is comparatively simple, it does not need to be governed by the factors we associate with feeding. Good drinking sites, particularly in dry weather, are just as dangerous as the feeding sites. Prey animals approach them with great caution in case a predator is lying in wait. But the act of drinking can be easily and quickly accomplished without relaxing vigilance too far. So most animals will drink even when they are too nervous to feed. They may even drink more when they are nervous. People drink enormous quantities of liquid at tense cocktail parties, but this also has something to do with our infancy.

All mammals go through a period of living entirely on liquid. This usually lasts as long as it takes for teeth to grow. As a class, we are unique in being able to suckle our young. Because we do, certain other things have followed. To suck, you must be able to create suction – you must have muscular cheeks and protrusible lips. So we grew some and found that they were useful in other ways. They greatly enhanced our ability to make changes in the configuration of our faces, and they are vital for our elaborate language of facial expression. The first face that any monkey or man makes is one in which the lips are pushed out in a pout. This begins as a movement designed to indicate the need to suckle, but it persists after weaning as an expression used when asking for attention or some sign of reassurance. Hence the confusion between drinking and the need for security – and the high consumption at cocktail parties.

Most adult animals continue to drink using the skills they learned while suckling. A few, like the big cats, have mouths too wide to suck easily and so they lap the liquid. Their tongues are covered with little furry projections which catch water. Elephants have trunks that hold two gallons at a time. Some species use fur as an aid to drinking. Gibbons drink by dipping their shaggy forearms into the water and sucking at the fur. Mongooses carry water home to their young by immersing the upper part of the body in a stream or pool. The most refined method is that used by the chimpanzee on occasions. They collect water out of hollow trees and narrow cracks by soaking it up in a handful of dry moss and squeezing the sponge out into their mouths.

There are few elaborate behaviour patterns associated with drinking, though some species are obliged by their anatomy to drink in a peculiar way. Giraffes have such long legs that they cannot get even their necks down to water without awkwardly spreading the forelimbs wide apart. Sable antelope have a heavy curve of horn which unbalances them unless they kneel to drink. Very often a water source is partly polluted by floating scum. Several of the hoofed animals deal with it by pawing at the surface to clear a space for drinking. Some, like the monkeys, actually clear it away with their hands. Most rely simply on the oil in their muzzles to break the surface tension and spread the layer of dirt away from them. Some men collect wax from their ears on a fingertip and dip this into the water for the same purpose.

Man has also developed many other ways of purifying water. He strains and filters it through sand and earthenware. He boils and distills it and treats it with chemicals. The first chemical agent was the seed of a fruit – probably a peach or a plum. Placed in cloudy water, these have a property which precipitates the mud.

But water is not the only liquid available. All mammals drink milk as babies. We are the only ones who continue drinking it as adults. Koala bear babies are weaned on a special gum leaf soup that they get directly from the mother's anus. A few animals drink fruit juices from time to time, but there is only one mammal which lives entirely on liquid. There is only one liquid that could provide a complete balanced diet. That liquid is blood and the animal is of course the vampire bat. This nightmare beast comes softly down near a sleeping body, partly folds its shrouds, and tiptoes over to feed. It has two razorlike upper incisors (not canines, as the horror films suggest) which are sharp enough to cut a shallow groove in most skins without waking the owner. As the wound fills with blood the vampire laps it with its tongue, drooling saliva into the open wound to prevent coagulation. Having drunk its fill, it creeps away, making (if we can believe the local donors) fiendish little cackling sounds.

Apart from Count Dracula, there are human blood drinkers. The nomadic Masai often mix milk with blood tapped from the jugular vein of one of their cows. A few men drink urine. But when we use the word 'drink' we more often than not mean alcohol. Ethyl alcohol – a poison taken internally by human beings for thousands of years. A substance so simple to make that it often makes itself. Ripe fruit lying in a watery mush at the base of a tree quickly ferments and forms alcohol. I have often seen elephants which have been feeding underneath one of these trees go charging off like runaway bulldozers, cutting great wavy paths through the bush. And warthogs, so drunk they could not hold their tails up, stagger off bumping blindly into every anthill. Early man got his first hangover in the same way, but it did not stop him from coming back for more.

The practice of drinking alcohol and of deliberately brewing it arose spontaneously in nearly every part of the world. With the exception of the Eskimo, every race produces some kind of alcoholic beverage. Early man drank it simply to get drunk, because it stimulated him. Later he discovered that alcohol could be made in several forms – and that some tasted better than others. In travelling after the herds of game, he came across new fruits and experimented with them – eventually discovering grapes. A producing vineyard takes several years to reach its peak, so he may have come back to it again and again. But, as an alternative to the theory that the large-grained grasses enticed man to settle down, I suggest that the grape might have had something to do with it. Perhaps man grew so fond of the vine that he was reluctant to let other animals get to its fruits before him and hung around to wait for the harvest. While waiting, he discovered the value of the grain growing nearby. Man might have been a brewer before he became a baker. But he would very soon have discovered that the cereals grown for baking could also be used for even more effective brewing.

Alcohol developed as an essential part of the agricultural complex. Its effects both pleased and puzzled the early drinking farmers. They soon began to associate its magical essence with the life force that governed the growth of their crops. Many people today still spill a little wine from every glass onto the soil to ensure its continued fertility. In the early farming communities drunkenness in honour of the grain god became a sacred duty. It unshackled man's mind and gave him the confidence he needed to begin thinking about the elements and the other things in his environment over which he had no control. It might have led to the development of an answer – a religion. Shamanism was the first organised religion, and as practised today by witch doctors, it is still almost entirely based on the fervour produced by intoxication. Remnants of the link between wine and worship survive in even the most modern religions.

The first historical reference to alcohol is in Babylonian tablets that include recipes. Wine was made in China 4,000 years ago and near Jerusalem at least 1,000 years before Christ. From the Middle East, the vine passed via the Phoenicians to Greece, to the Etruscans, on to Rome and into the Empire after Caesar's conquest of Gaul. It even preceded Europeans to America; when Leif Ericson arrived, he found vines growing luxuriously there, so he called it Vinland.

Eventually, recognition that there was something potent in wine led to the search for its essence through distillation. Gin, cognac and whisky were the first spirits. Soon followed by rum, a drink that founded fortunes, built cities, and financed a slave trade. It also virtually started the American Revolution when New Englanders, objecting to the high duty on imports of molasses, began to smuggle rum. This bothered the British customs a great deal more than tea.

Alcohol is one of the few substances absorbed directly into the blood stream. It is an anaesthetic causing progressive paralysis of the nervous system. Drink enough and you fall asleep; drink too much and you never wake up. An overdose of water or oxygen also produces intoxication, but alcohol is unique in the effect it has on the brain. It heightens both awareness and unawareness. In its early stages it increases and intensifies sociability and communication, knocking out those areas in the brain concerned with inhibition. In the later stages, awareness is decreased in a behavioural confusion that ends in oblivion. Biologically, this means that alcohol first produces exploratory tendencies, giving confidence to explore new territories and new ideas. And then it turns the evolutionary clock back, making it uncomfortable to explore. So it caters in different concentrations to both specialist and opportunist. As we all have something of each in our make-up, alcohol can cater to everyone. Small wonder that it is so popular.

Drinking has a social as well as a physiological function. Nearly all animals need free water, and as it occurs in only one natural liquid form, they have to go to the same places to get it. Every naturalist knows that the best place to see the largest number of species is at the local waterhole. It is the only place where animals, otherwise scattered over a wide area, are likely to meet. This may not mean much to most species, but it has meant a great deal to man. He met and exchanged both blows and ideas at primitive watering places. He found there the stimulus he needed to progress in new directions. Modern waterholes are little different; they still serve as the centres of community activity – places where people get together to discuss things over a cup or a glass.

The social function of drinking reached its greatest level of sophistication among the Japanese. The tea ceremony of *chanoyu* is now an elaborate ritual built around twenty-four separate schools of thought, each with its own long genealogy of tea masters. The ritual involves a variety of instruments, each of which is used in a carefully prescribed fashion. The subtle movements involved are all symbolic, with bearings on religion, literature, philosophy and art. The most complex form of the ritual is used as a temple ceremony, but basically the tea party is a social occasion. All the postures involved (guests have to enter the teahouse through a door only two feet high) stress appeasement and conciliation. The host kneels to greet his guests, and they reciprocate with formal admiration of the features used in decoration. Commercial teahouses are given self-deprecatory names like *Karoan*, which is 'a mean little hut'.

The spread of the tea habit, with green tea in Burma, salt tea in Siam, bitter tea in Kashmir, cream tea in Turkestan and weak tea in England, is partly due to the beverage itself, which contains more habit-forming caffeine than coffee. But mainly due to the fact that it has everywhere been accompanied by a ceremony or a ritual of some kind acting as a force of social cohesion.

Drinking for all mammals involves far less dexterity and concentration than eating. There is therefore less risk of being caught off guard by a predator or rival. All animals feel less tense at a drinking site than they do at a feeding site. And so no complex instincts have had to be developed to deal with the intake of liquid. Man still feels table tension but is perfectly relaxed in pubs and bars. He goes there to relax and find security. Some of the security is due to the association between the maternal breast and the drinking vessel. Most cups and many glasses are obviously breast-shaped. (We even refer to the cups of brassieres.) But this association probably becomes less important with increasing age. Drinking straws, which involve active sucking, are much more popular with younger children. In adult life, the fraternal value of drinking takes over from the maternal. And the consumption of water, plus various additives, assumes as much psychological as physiological importance. Men go out to drink with the boys, women go to tea with the girls. And the invitation from boy to girl is far more often 'Can I get you a drink' than 'Can I feed you?'

Eating and drinking often go together, but they are quite distinct patterns of behaviour, with independent origins and goals.

EIGHT

FOOD AND SEX

There is a wonderful science fiction story called F ——. It tells of a time when the refinement of contraceptive techniques has made sex readily and freely available. Eating, on the other hand, has been made obsolete by similar refinements in nutritional pills. So food becomes the taboo subject and pictures of exciting pieces of roast beef are peddled as pornography.

It sounds bizarre but is in fact a distinct biological possibility. There are any number of ways in which food and sex are closely linked. A few animals have trouble telling them apart. Amongst some web-building spiders, the male visits the female on her web. He has to go through an incredible semaphore performance with his legs in order to appease her and make quite sure she does not mistake him for her prey. If his signals get through, she may allow him to get close enough to copulate. But he cannot afford to relax for a moment. Male spiders which hang around too long afterwards frequently get eaten by their mates.

Sex makes people hungry. The reverse is also true. Food makes people sexy. Most foods at one time or another have been regarded as aphrodisiacs. Even sweet potatoes and chocolate were sold as stimulants when they first arrived in Europe. Tomatoes were thought to be the original forbidden fruit when explorers brought them back from South America. For many years they were called love apples. The frantic search for truffles, the training of special truffle hounds to seek them out, and the high prices paid for these fungi are based on a long-standing belief that they increase the size of the genitals. The oldest recorded use of an aphrodisiac appears in Genesis where Rachel, in desperation, feeds mandrakes to impotent old Jacob. It seemed to work, and ever since the search has gone on for other and more potent ways of getting to a man's heart through his stomach. Some recent recipes include oysters, asparagus, pollen of date palm, tigers' testicles, turtles' eggs, pine nuts, bats' blood, rhinos' horn, swallows' heart, the tissue of a camel's hump and the gall of a spastic child. The only bed such concoctions are likely to lead to is one in a hospital.

There is absolutely no evidence that any foodstuff is capable of acting specifically as a sexual stimulant. But, in a sense, all food is aphrodisiac. Eating causes an increase in the pulse rate and the blood pressure, raises the body temperature, and may even produce sweating. In all these things it exactly simulates the physiological changes which take place prior to an orgasm. This was demonstrated to perfection in a recent film in which the two lovers sat opposite each other at a small table by candlelight and, in the process of dismembering and eating a chicken, worked themselves up to such a frenzy that they had to abandon the meal altogether.

There are many overtly sexy foods and all of them are very popular. Things like bananas, eels, carrots and sausages are obviously phallic. There is even one, the champagne bottle, which ejaculates when it is opened. This accounts in large part for the popularity of champagne at those special little dinners for two. A meal in attractive surroundings has become a standard part of seduction scenes in many parts of the world. There are direct parallels among animals which indulge in courtship feeding displays.

These begin with a breeding situation in which it is necessary for the male to become very aggressive towards other males. He has to threaten or actually fight them to establish a breeding territory or to collect a group of breeding females. To avoid being attacked themselves, the females have to differ in some way from the males. In many species they have different colours or physical structures which make them clearly distinct. But in others the appearance is so similar that females have to show special behaviour patterns to suppress the male's aggressiveness. One of the most common and effective methods is for the female to behave in an infantile way. If she seems to be young, by resorting to the same patterns of appeasement that are employed by the young, then the male will not attack her. His aggression will be replaced by his parental drive, and he may even go as far as actually feeding her as though she were young and helpless.

Male herring gulls respond to the begging posture of the female by regurgitating food for her. Hunting dogs and wolves react to appeasement by regurgitating a little food that is licked out of the side of the male's mouth by the female. Active male courtship frequently involves bringing the female an unsolicited food gift. Some spiders approach potential mates with the present of a fly neatly wrapped up in a ball of silk. While the female is feeding, the male takes his chance and quickly copulates. Human suitors come similarly armed with boxes of chocolates.

In most cases it is the male which feeds the female, but there is one situation in which the roles are reversed. In a harem, one man is surrounded by a number of women. They are put in a position of having to court him for his favours. There is rivalry between the women which makes them aggressive towards each other. To prevent this aggression from being turned against him, the man makes gestures of appeasement. In the same way that a female gull goes one stop down the dominance ladder by becoming juvenile, the harem keeper steps down by adopting a female posture. He lies on his back on a pile of cushions and leaves courtship feeding to the women. They ply him with sweetmeats and drop handpicked grapes into his open mouth.

In these examples we see food being used as a means to sexual seduction, but sex often is equally used as an inducement to feed. A popular series of posters on British Railways showed a girl looking seductively out over the caption 'Don't just stand there, eat something!' Most food manufacturers sooner or later get around to advertising their product with the aid of sex. They may indirectly do it by using sexual symbolism in the display or by suggesting directly that the product promises to put the consumer in a sexual situation. 'Come alive with X' and 'Things go better with Y'. Restaurants have always used attractive serving wenches to help sell their food. Some have recently exploited this technique even more thoroughly by having their girls go topless. Bottomless waitresses would be even more daring but not nearly as successful. There is a very basic connection between breasts and feeding.

Breasts began as structures designed only for feeding. In most primates they still are rather flat swellings with elongated nipples. Shapes much better adapted for lactation than our exaggerated, rounded breasts which make it difficult for the baby to get the nipple far enough into his mouth. But human breasts are now concerned not only with feeding. They have become sexual signalling devices, and along with all the most effective signals, they exaggerate the message. They produce a supernormal stimulus that provides supernormal responses. The same thing has happened to foods designed by man. The designer wants them to sell well, so he incorporates features which exaggerate those characteristics that a buyer associates with the food. The housewife believes that specks of dirt on an egg show it has directly come from the farmyard, so the shops market highly speckled eggs. The shopper expects fresh meat to be red, so butchers touch up display joints with a bright-red cosmetic colouring. Exactly the same substance now being sold as nipple rouge for making female breasts even more attractive to the male customer.

Both breasts and mouths originated as organs for feeding, but both have gone on to become major erogenous zones. They form the first and one of the most basic links between two systems of behaviour that are now indistinguishable in many ways. Food and sex even share a whole list of descriptive terms. 'Appetite', 'hunger', 'satisfaction', 'satiated', 'starved', can all apply equally well to our needs for food or for each other. We often use idioms drawn from one system to describe activities in the other. 'They met at one of the fleshpots.' 'She looked delicious.' 'He devoured her with his eyes.'

There are direct parallels between the uses of food and sex. Feeding began as an activity directed only towards providing the body with adequate nutrition. Mating at first served only for procreation. Today we eat without being hungry and copulate without producing children. There are vast areas of non-nutritional feeding and non-procreational sex. The emancipation of each of these basic systems from its primary function has opened up large areas of secondary activity.

Both food and sex now have social functions. One we have already looked at briefly is courtship feeding. This makes food an aid to pair formation. Like the mutual grooming of monkeys, it brings male and female into close proximity in a situation where they can be reasonably relaxed and where offensive and defensive tactics need not be called into play. The ritual of choosing food and dealing with it provides a valuable diversion which gives the pair bond time to form in neutral territory. Courting males, however, do everything they can to gain a small advantage by laying claim to the territory as their own. They cultivate pseudo-relationships with the restaurateur. If he is wise, he plays along and makes a point of greeting them by name when they come in with a new mouth to feed. He will also remember what the courtship feeder had to drink on previous occasions so that he can produce it when the male, as part of his display, airily asks for the usual. Many male courting animals sing or call to attract a female's attention. The sort of restaurants which cater largely to courtship feeders often have a professional on hand to do the singing for them. Singing waiters are as popular as topless waitresses. If the feeder is giving a full-dress display, he will find out what the female most likes to hear and make sure she sees that it is he who calls the tune.

Once a pair bond has been formed by food and sex, it can be maintained in the same way. The relationship is reinforced by more elaborate and inventive sexual activity and by a new kind of feeding. Courtship feeding is replaced by domestic feeding, and the initiative passes from male into female hands.

There is no way in which a woman can more easily express her feelings towards her mate than through the food she prepares for him. This type of feeding is a powerful way of cementing an existing pair bond. It takes place more often than sex. When members of a pair are separated from each other for some time, they typically celebrate the reunion by going out to dinner. Courtship feeding reappears, along with heightened sexual activity, to renew the strength of the bond.

Domestic feeding applies not only to the mate. A mother reaches her whole family through the medium of a meal. If she provides a particular type of food which requires special preparation or is difficult to obtain, she is expressing her love for them in a very tangible way. Over a period of time these special dishes, regardless of their nutritive value, come to symbolise a certain relationship inside the family group. No amount of education or propaganda can ever shake the family's faith in that symbolism. No one can ever make it quite the way mother did. Modern food advertisers are very much aware of the tradition and try to bend it to their own ends. There are few television commercials for food that do not have a child with a spoon in his hand, brand X in his mouth and love in his eyes for mother.

Not surprisingly, the foodstuff with most mum value is milk. Young soldiers returning home after World War II told of their enormous desire for milk. One of the first things they did, as soon as it was available, was to drink several quarts at a single sitting. It is possible that they were responding to a deficiency in their bodies, but most of them were physically healthy. What milk had to offer them was not calcium but motherly comfort and security. Milk has no sleep-inducing properties, yet it is often taken (usually at body temperature) at bedtime. What is more comforting for an anxious insomniac than warm milk before he curls up in an infantile position to sleep?

Food and sex are closely linked with all kinds of hospitality. Both can be bought but are valued much more highly if freely given. Eskimos make a point of offering a welcome stranger both food and the favours of their wives. A man's social standing depends on his ability to make these offers. Of the two, food is the most important. Almost everywhere, food and hospitality are regarded as synonymous. Feeding not only helps form a pair bond but assists in creating bonds between any two people. It puts strangers at their ease. This function of food is so familiar that we feel uneasy eating alone. It was not always so.

Many modern mammals still eat alone – and for them the meal has little extra value. A stoat catches mice, birds or fish and eats them on the spot. It eats purely to live. Otters are more social, hunting and eating together. Their mealtimes are occasions for mock battles and acrobatic water sports, often involving the food itself as part of the game. Coyotes and foxes usually hunt alone, and for them food is food. Some of their feeding patterns – such as the special stiff-legged 'mouse leap' – may be used in play with each other, but food is used only for eating. Wolves and hunting dogs, on the other hand, hunt together in packs and share their food. Hunting dogs regurgitate chunks to form a communal food pile, and wolves use food as a peace offering in social and sexual situations.

Man once was a solitary feeder, but he became a pack hunter and has never gone back to eating alone. For us eating is a group activity. We refer to 'breaking bread together'. In modern slang, to 'chew the fat' with someone is to get together for a sociable talk. The emphasis is on food sharing. It began as a survival mechanism and is still obligatory in the hunting communities. In Eskimo or Bushman society it would be unthinkable to eat a delicacy without sharing it equally among all those present.

Even after it ceased to be a necessity, food sharing was maintained as a tradition. In our frantic Western society, formalities have been reduced to a minimum. A visitor can expect little more than a drink of something unless specifically invited to dine. But, almost everywhere else, food-offering ceremonies are still elaborate and important. If a visitor arrives unexpectedly at a Pedi kraal in South Africa, no matter what time of day, the woman of the house will automatically begin cleaning the pot to prepare a meal, until she is stopped by the guest's courteous refusal. Among the Bedouins, refusal is impossible. Hospitality also extends to the parting guest who, in many countries, is offered a small gift of grain or meat to take with him. This is not intended to tide him over the journey but to enable him to prove to the people at home that he was well received. In most places the meal is a leisurely sociable affair. To hurry through it is to show disrespect.

As a guest, one is expected to conform to an elaborate ritual, which is closely related to the system of signals and responses characteristic of social-greeting displays in animals. Monkeys offer their posteriors, apes offer the back of their hands, and we offer food. In the Gilbert Islands, the ritual is very precise. The host passes an item of food to the guest with the words 'You shall be blessed.' The guest immediately returns both the blessing and the food. The host then takes the first courtesy taste from the dish and passes the food, this time with both hands, back to the guest. After eating, the guest returns his empty plate and belches loudly to show that the food was well received. An additional point of honour is to present exactly the right amount of food. Too much is regarded as bad catering and too little as a sign of meanness. In Asian and African communities the ritual may differ in small details, but the emphasis is still placed on courtesy and friendship through the performance of traditional feeding displays.

The meal therefore symbolises friendship, cementing existing social ties and making new ones by putting strangers at their ease. But it can also have many other symbolic values, by allowing all sorts of roles to be played. Common ones are the careful housewife, the much-travelled connoisseur, the perfect host and the vegetarian moralist. Food, like sex, can have a status value.

Harem overlords used to collect and display as many wives as they could manage. The man who was seen to have the largest number was considered to be the most powerful. Food provides a similar index of status. It may do so by a simple display of quantity. The Trobriand islander who has the largest pile of yams holds a position in the community which is beyond question. But today it is more often quality which determines the status of the food and the feeder. In every society there are foods that are rare or expensive or both. Status-seeking hosts will go to enormous trouble and expense to provide these items for their guests. The exact nature of the desired foods depends on their availability at that time and place. In wartime Germany, all a host needed to do was produce butter. But today it has to be something like *Trockenbeerenauslese*, a wine produced from grapes that have a special mould growing on them. The fact that it takes a skilled picker a whole day to find enough of these grapes to produce just one bottle of wine makes it a perfect and expensive status food.

Status foods work at all levels. They often identify a family group and place them in their correct, or desired, social pigeon-hole. In East Pakistan a salaried man and his family do not eat red rice. In Mexico they abandon the traditional tortilla in favour of white bread. If the group are eating away from home, they are equally careful to choose an eating place of the correct status. They identify it by certain unmistakable, but quite arbitrary, signals. In England one of the best signals is the tablecloth. Low-priced workingmen's cafés seldom have cloths on the tables. Middle-priced restaurants for middle-class people nearly always do. And some of the really high-priced restaurants have undisputed top status, so they can afford to dispense with the usual signals and return again to serving meals on bare boards.

One final illustration of the social functions of sex and food is facilitation. We have already seen that two animals feeding together will each eat more than when they feed apart. The same is true of breeding together. Communal courtship has the effect of bringing all the participants into peak reproductive condition much more quickly. We know that human eating is socially facilitated because we eat readily and well in large groups. But there is not yet enough good information to show that sex in our species is also socially facilitated. The few extrovert people who experiment with group sex give such enthusiastic reports that it may well be.

The next most important secondary function of food and sex is that they both provide therapy. Mating, for instance, is a vital bodily function that needs to have an outlet. If it is not satisfied by normal copulation, tension builds up and has to be relieved in some other way. One widespread solution is masturbation. We have seen how raccoons suffer tension when deprived of the opportunity to perform a basic feeding activity. The raccoon's way of relieving tension (its method of 'masturbating') is to take its food to water. Humans can relieve tension in the same way by performing feeding patterns that have no connection with normal feeding behaviour. When we are tense, we go through the motions of feeding by chewing gum or by sucking smoke through a cigarette. Both actions help to lower tension by the performance of a familiar action pattern. Neither gum nor tobacco provides us with any nutritional value. They are examples of oral masturbation.

One of the most common causes of tension is fear of the unknown. An animal which starts to explore an unfamiliar area always moves slowly, with a rather jerky action. It makes a foray out into the unknown and then dashes back to the security of a place it knows better. Then it starts out again and perhaps gains a little more ground this time, before having to dash back again to safety. The whole procedure can be very long and drawn out unless the animal finds a better way to build confidence. One of the best ways of finding security, if you cannot afford to go back to a familiar place, is to do a familiar thing. Few things are more familiar than patterns of feeding, and so these are most often called into play. An acouchy (the long-legged guinea pig) breaking new ground shows all the symptoms of fear and makes slow progress until it comes across a piece of food. It need only be something that vaguely resembles its normal food to do the trick. It stops, picks it up, and then goes through the whole elaborate hoarding pattern of digging a hole and burying it. This works wonders. Having done the familiar thing, it continues to explore with much greater confidence. A man enjoys the same benefits by resorting to the ritual of lighting a cigarette. He is put at ease not so much by the narcotic effect of the nicotine as by the elaborate performance itself. It works just as well with fake cigarettes containing no tobacco at all.

Another common type of tension is the conflict that can be caused by sex. This also can be resolved by feeding. When two evenly matched males meet in a dispute over breeding territory or over a mate, they begin to threaten each other. Threat displays are brought about by conflict between fighting and fleeing. Neither male is motivated strongly enough to attack or to run away, so they stand locked in a confrontation that cannot be easily resolved. At these times, feeding often appears and provides a safe diversion for the pent-up energy. For instance, two male antelope of equal size and status may be circling each other with their bodies stiff and tense, pawing the ground, nodding and blowing through their nostrils. Suddenly the impasse breaks and both of them begin nibbling at nearby bushes. A few moments later they are back circling again, but the intrusion of displacement feeding has taken the edge off their aggression and reduced the risk of injury in actual combat. We adopt the same strategy. It is very common for people whose tensions stem from social insecurity to indulge in displacement feeding.

Refugee children taken to the United States in the years immediately prior to World War II gorged themselves in the land of plenty. Once installed in a home with affection and security, their intake of food fell back to the normal level. But their emotional balance was still highly precarious. If at any time the children were threatened with insecurity – such as a decrease in attention from their foster parents – their food intake soared again to a supernormal level. This sort of response can persist throughout life. There is a direct correlation between adult fatness and childhood insecurity. The laughing fat man was probably once a miserable child.

There is one more way in which food and sex can be therapeutic. They can help an animal that is not tense enough. They give a bored or inactive individual something to do. It can stimulate itself sexually or copulate with someone or nibble away at things to pass the time. If there is nothing to bite but fingernails, then these are chewed away as fast as they grow. This kind of non-nutritional feeding can develop into pathological habits like eating faeces or swallowing safety pins; but if food is available, then a lot of it is eaten. Comfort is found both in the food itself and in the act of eating it.

Omnivores are animals which enjoy experimenting with new foods and new tastes. They also tend to explore in other ways and to have a more varied and interesting sex life. Man, as a superomnivore, not only eats more different foods than any other animal but also has more complex sex practices. We can enjoy food and sex for their own sake and we do so in an enormous variety of ways. There are epicures and libertines who make an art of this enjoyment – and gluttons and debauchers who take it to excess. Feeding is still important for nutrition and sex for reproduction, but it is impossible to equate salad dressings and sauces or frilly nightdresses and perfumes with these simple primary functions. They are secondary embellishments we omnivores add to things we enjoy to make them a little different and even more enjoyable.

The development of our abilities to appreciate fine food and sex follow parallel lines. There are sex differences in body odours which only begin to show at puberty. Connected with these, there is a marked change in odour preferences. A shift from sweet to musky smells. This once had a purely sexual significance, but the senses of smell and taste are so closely linked that the shift now appears also in patterns of feeding. Children who once would eat nothing but ice cream and sugar confections suddenly become more interested in the wider range of salty, bitter and oily flavours. They begin to enjoy pickles and chutneys, lemons, oysters and foods cooked in olive oil. All the things we sometimes describe as an acquired taste. This maturation of the palate appears earlier in girls, who come to puberty about two years before their brothers. Both sexes show a corresponding decline in sexual activity and in the sensitivity of the palate with old age.

Some food likes and dislikes have nothing to do with maturation. Almost everyone has a short list of foods which they like very much or violently dislike. These appetites appear as the result of a process called imprinting. The aversions are due to traumatic experiences. Some birds are programmed so that they become socially imprinted permanently on the first large moving object they see during the short critical period following hatching. In controlled experiments, chicks have been imprinted on football boots and packs of cigarettes. When they reach sexual maturity, these are the things they seek out and try to mate with. Our food preferences are often determined in a similar way. As children, we enjoyed certain foods because of their associations. We liked the person who first gave them to us, or we first ate them in a place where we felt happy and secure. We also came to dislike other foods because we had bad experiences with them. Perhaps we became sick as a result of eating too much. The result of these experiences during a formative period is that we become positively imprinted on the foods or negatively biased against them. And we continue to enjoy or avoid them forever.

Early experience can also completely change the quality of our response to normal stimuli. It can turn us into perverts – people who do not enjoy things in the normal way. Sexual perversions abound and are well catalogued by pornography and psychiatry. But food perversions have been completely neglected. For each one of the well-known sexual perversions, there is a comparable deviation in feeding behaviour.

We have already discussed oral masturbation. There is also oral voyeurism. It takes place outside every restaurant with a plate glass window in a poor neighbourhood. In fact, we need not be hungry to become oral voyeurs. One of the underground film directors recently produced a full-length feature film of a man eating a lobster in slow motion. The sequence where he finally extracts a juicy piece of flesh from the big claw nearly always provokes spontaneous applause from the audience. Then there is oral sadism which is practised by every parent who persistently puts non-nutritious things like turnips in front of an unwilling child. 'It is for your own good, dear.' 'This hurts me more than it hurts you.' If the child is actually fed by force on the unwanted food, this is clearly a case of oral rape. There should be a law against it. Forced feeding of geese to produce *pâté de foie gras*, or of calves to produce white veal, is rape committed on an animal – oral bestiality.

Some fairly normal sex practices can be considered as technical perversions because they do not lead to conception. Feeding perversions are those that do not lead to nutrition. So the

Romans practised oral contraception. They went through the whole feeding sequence, even consummating the meal by swallowing the food. But then they aborted it with a feather and started all over again on another dish. In the same vein, oral *coitus interruptus* is the perversion of wine tasters, who spit out the food before swallowing it. Oral celibacy is shown by those who go on voluntary fasts. There is usually a religious motive, but the practice can never be carried on as long as sexual celibacy. Complete oral celibates lead very short lives. Involuntary oral celibacy is unfortunately becoming far too widespread as millions all over the world are forced to fast until they die of starvation.

There are of course oral exhibitionists who drink or eat vast quantities for effect. There was even a recent craze for swallowing live goldfish. The food itself may be involved in exhibitionism. Traditionally, all the early stages of food preparation are done in private in the kitchen, and the dish is only allowed to appear in public when it is properly dressed. But there is a growing number of restaurants which do all the preparation in public. The chefs conduct a sort of striptease by dismembering the meat in full view of the customers. Television programmes take enormous numbers of viewers behind the scenes to the formerly forbidden territory of great kitchens, where every secret of food preparation is layed bare by popular impresarios.

Oral fetishism occurs, but it is much more complex. The field includes obvious fetishists like the child who will not part with his dummy. And many other examples which go on into the realm of food taboos. Cannibalism, for instance, could also be called oral incest. The practice of eating your own is directly analogous to the practice of mating with your own. There are widespread taboos against both. Many societies also have rules against sexual relations with members of your own sex, but it is interesting that none has taboos against people of the same sex eating together. They would be too difficult to enforce. Where homosexuality is an accepted practice, there is often an insistence on the sexes eating separately as well. Among the Masai, a young warrior is forbidden to eat any meat that has even been seen by a woman. One of the greatest insults to a warrior translates literally as 'eater of meat that was seen by your mother'.

All the evidence points to the fact that both food and sex are basic activities firmly fixed at the lowest behavioural level – and therefore often inseparable. It could be argued that sex is far more basic, as more emphasis is placed on it in nearly every aspect of our lives. But this is a product of our own peculiar Western culture in which sex is strictly controlled. Our preoccupation with sex stems from the fact that, as a commodity, it is still relatively scarce. Anthropological studies on African tribes in which sex is abundant and food is scarce show that food dominates the subconscious of a food-hungry people and that their cultures and traditions are hardly concerned with sex at all. The answer seems to be that both systems are important and that a human culture is shaped according to the relative abundance of each. A society in which both food and sex were controlled would need to be very complex indeed.

The most disturbing connection between food and sex is that the primary functions of each are incompatible. Procreative sex works directly against nutritional feeding by producing more mouths than the available food supplies can fill. The species needs both systems, but some individuals have to do without one or the other. At the moment, the majority are doing without food and finding it fatal. The consequences of doing without reproduction are never so dire. It is high time more of us opted for this alternative.

NINE

FOOD FOR THOUGHT

Food disappears as we eat. We swallow and it is gone. A long sequence of behaviour reaches its climax; but the game does not end there.

For many mammals, such as the insect eaters, the meal itself is never-ending. It is made up of an enormous number of tiny feeding sequences. Search, find, investigate, prepare, and eat – each one complete in itself, but only part of a much longer life-long performance. When all the time is mealtime, the only effect the meal can have is to keep the eater alive. This is the first and most important effect of feeding. Others appear later when an animal develops some sort of feeding speciality that makes it more efficient and more mobile.

One of the least-considered effects of food is its influence on the relationships between species. In Africa there is a badgerlike animal called the ratel. It has a tough skin and powerful claws and wanders around in bush country, living on beetles, snakes and small mammals – and all the time looking for honey to which it is particularly partial. In the same area lives a small brown bird which eats insects and grubs but, like the ratel, has a passion for honey. The local source of honey is a wild bee which builds nests in tree trunks and crevices. The bird finds these easily enough but cannot get inside them. The ratel has claws strong enough to rip the nests open but has difficulty finding them. So they join forces. The bird looks for a ratel and when it finds one, begins to chatter loudly and persistently. The ratel moves towards the bird, making chuckling and hissing sounds in reply. The honey guide, for that is its name, leads the ratel directly to the nest, waits while it breaks it open and eats its fill, and then joins in the feast. Lately, the honey guide has discovered that man can usually be relied upon to provide the same cooperative service, and it often tries to entice him to a hive in the same way.

In southwest New Guinea there is a tribe of fishermen who have a similar working arrangement with the local dolphins. The men go out each morning to a particular cove and slap their oars on the water. Dolphins suddenly arrive and swim in front of the boats until they find a shoal of fish, which they herd into a compact mass. The men run a net around the fish and haul them into the boats, pausing every now and then to throw a particularly tasty one to the dolphins, who gather around with their heads out of the water to watch the whole performance. The interaction seems to be every bit as rewarding to them as the fish they receive.

In both of these examples, the common factor forming the bond between the species is food. Most associations between widely different animal species are based on a better feeding deal for one or both of the associates. All the close relationships between our species and the animals which we have domesticated began with our offering them food. The connection between food and friendship in our minds is so close that it has already caused one misunderstanding.

Opportunist animals in dull zoos are forced to create their own variety. They find the best potential source of interest in the people who pass by, and they perform all sorts of outlandish behaviour patterns to attract our attention. With our often surprisingly limited imagination, we assume that they must be begging for food, so we ply them with buns and sticky sweets. To keep us there responding, they have to reward us by eating at least part of the rubbish we throw their way. And so every day animals in zoos die of overeating when all they really lack is attention.

I am one of those who believe that sooner or later we are going to meet another species at least as intelligent as we are.

And I hope that when it happens we are not going to prejudice the success of the first crucial meeting by our overwhelming obsession with food. It could so easily be disastrously misunderstood.

Food has had an enormous influence on our social behaviour. But our societies have also played a big part in determining food habits. We have already seen how a food-washing tradition is growing up in one colony of Japanese monkeys. In human societies there are any number of similar habits being formed. Racial, religious and traditional factors all shape food preferences – most often by determining what we shall not eat. Many foods are placed under a taboo, a strong social custom which forbids them to be eaten. The taboo leads to avoidance and this eventually becomes abhorrence, so the food is still not eaten long after the taboo and the reasons for it are forgotten.

Many taboos have their origin in health factors and clearly once had high survival value. The Western taboo against eating oysters in any month without an R in it once served a practical purpose. It ensured that the shellfish would be avoided in the warmest months of the year when they might be toxic. Today oysters are refrigerated and there is no risk at any time of year, but we still obey the taboo – even in the Southern Hemisphere. It is illogical, but who expects logic from a race which favours game and cheese that have partly decomposed – and yet discards beef or butter that is not completely fresh?

Of all food taboos, those enforced by the Jewish religion are among the most specific. The law of Moses lays down that Jews may eat any animal which has a cloven foot and chews the cud, anything in the water which has fins and scales, and all winged insects that are also able to leap. This eliminates pigs (whose meat spoils very quickly in a warm climate), camels (far too valuable as beasts of burden to be eaten), poisonous toads, scorpions and centipedes. The code had clear survival value for a small group of people in the limited area they then occupied. But it has been preserved intact and passed on to a large number of people in habitats where it has no relevance. In theory, Jews everywhere are forbidden to eat pork, bacon, ham, oysters, mussels, prawns, snails, pheasant, grouse, and rabbit. In practice, only the most orthodox still follow the letter of the law.

Moslems have similar taboos. They have one against eating 'anything which has died of itself' that makes sense anywhere at any time. But it is difficult to imagine why they should not be allowed to boil a kid in its mother's milk. They share the pork taboo with the Jakuts, Malagasy tribes, the Lapps and many red Indians. And they share their less logical prejudices with people all over the world. Fowl are taboo for Mongols and for the Indians of Guyana. Beef is forbidden for Hindu and Parsi. Hare is never eaten in China or by any old Breton. Eggs are scorned by the Waganda, Bahune and old Caribbees. Milk is poison to Dyaks, Malays, Dravidians and the Ashanti. In most instances, the taboo food may not have played a large part in their diet anyway – but some taboos have had very adverse effects. Zulus die of malnutrition on the banks of rivers full of forbidden fish.

In some instances, social factors have brought about some strange food preferences. Rotten eggs are delicacies in Brunei. Rice eaten by Sandy Lake Indians is seasoned with rabbit droppings. Eskimos of Coronation Gulf thicken their soup with the droppings of caribou. The Obbs of central Africa wash their milk bowls out with urine. In parts of Hungary, it is used for washing out the mouth. Of all people, the Tierra del Fuegians are the least particular. They eat absolutely everything, alive or long since dead, but they seem to be particularly fond of their own old women. They may be the last of a rare breed of feeders – the people eaters.

Cannibalism goes back at least to Peking man. More recently, there are records of it in Ireland in the first century BC, in Scotland in the fourth century, and in Spain in the ninth. In 1564, the Polish hero Wisniowiecki was defeated by the Turks, who tore out and ate his heart. In eastern Europe and Asia it was common for state executioners to retain as their perquisite the bodies of their victims. In Bohemia the Zingaris ate human flesh well into the eighteenth century – showing a preference for the ears, the palms of the hands and the soles of the feet. In the nineteenth century European explorers were eaten in Africa, South America and the Pacific. The ones who got away reported that chiefs in Fiji had cannibal feasts whenever they had their hair cut; that young mothers of the Uruguayan Chavantes ate their first-born; that victims in Nigeria were dismembered alive at jungle shrines; and that there was a saying in the Amazon to the effect that 'It is better to be inside a friend than to be swallowed up by the cold earth.'

Most universal of cannibal beliefs was that by eating another man one could acquire his 'soul stuff'. A man who ate the heart of a brave warrior would inherit his courage. The child of a skilled tracker would acquire the skills of his father by eating some part of his dead parent's flesh. All these are cannibal practices for superstitious reasons; they do not reflect the normal diet of the people involved. True nutritional cannibalism – man eating man because he likes to – is much rarer. But it did, and still does, happen.

In the Congo slaves were deliberately fattened up for sale in the markets as food. In Australia bodies were smoke-dried to tide the aborigines over lean times. In west Africa some tribes sold the corpses of their dead to other tribes. In South America one tribe actually kept a number of captive women who were induced to breed in order to ensure a regular supply of food. The variations are endless, but the important point is that all of these practices attracted notice simply because they were exceptional. Cannibalism has never been really popular.

There is a mechanism that stops, or tends to stop, man and other mammals from eating members of their own species. In all the wealth of zoological literature, there are very few reliable records of cannibalism. Of these, most are instances of starving animals falling on a dead or badly injured conspecific. Or of neurotic (usually captive) mothers devouring their own young. In these circumstances, the objects being eaten have lost their identity as species members because of a dramatic change in the environment. The hungry pack animals or the frightened mother have the threshold of their normal resistance to cannibalism lowered by an unusual experience. It is probably significant that several of the animals accused of cannibalism, like the wolf and the weasel, have a bad reputation with man anyway. It is certainly significant that the few other records of animal cannibalism all concern either pigs or bears – both omnivores.

If the anticannibal mechanism is an instinct, it need apply only to carnivores, and it must be strongest in those carnivores which are the most efficient killers. Without it, they would simply kill and eat each other and there would be no lions, tigers or wolves. With it, they are able to distinguish rival from prey and can fight members of their own species without using their special killing techniques. Herbivores, because they seldom if ever eat meat, do not need and do not have an anticannibal device.

Only with the omnivores is there any chance of confusion. Omnivores eat meat, but they cannot kill large prey animals to get it. Because they are not armed with dangerous weapons that could be turned against their own kind, they do not have an inhibition against doing this. And if they should come across a dead member of their own species, they have no block against eating it. So pigs and bears (except for the completely carnivorous polar bear) sometimes become cannibals. But it happens only as often as they chance to come across a dead pig or bear the predators have missed. That is very seldom.

Man was once a herbivore without the need or the means to kill. But he then became a hunter and developed weapons as destructive as those of any carnivore. With these, he was able to kill other men easily. We know he did and we know he ate them. But if this had gone unchecked, there would soon have been no men left to eat or be eaten. So carnivorous man developed the carnivore's taboo. The taboo against killing and eating one's own kind.

This severely limited the occurrence of cannibalism but failed to eliminate it altogether because of our unique history. We came from unarmed herbivore to armed carnivore quickly, so we did not have enough time to develop the proper safeguards. Instead of going through the tens of millions of years necessary to develop big teeth and sharp claws, we short-circuited the whole process and acquired spears and daggers in a few hundred thousand years. We got killing weapons without the usual instinctive inhibition against using them on ourselves. All we have is a taboo enforced by moral and religious opinion. This goes some way towards preventing us all from eating one another; it works particularly well with members of the same group, tribe or race. But it is not nearly strong enough to prevent man from frequently killing other men – and occasionally eating them.

Allied to the cannibal's ritual practice of eating his enemies' hearts are similar beliefs associated with other animals. To be strong, one has to eat a lion; to see in the dark, one eats the eyes of an owl. It has recently been discovered that one can teach planarian flatworms simple responses, such as travelling through a light and dark maze to find food. If one then chops the worms up into small pieces and feeds them to other untrained flatworms, the second group learns to do the tricks much more quickly. So it is just possible that the superstitious beliefs about eating what you want to be are not so naïve after all. One interesting exception to the philosophy is that fish are nowhere considered to be very bright – and yet their flesh is widely held to be the best of brain foods. The answer may be that the two are associated because their textures and consistencies are somewhat similar.

We have looked so far at food as food – and at foods that have a non-food value as a result of social or biological pressures. But the opposite is also possible. Substances with no food value at all can be eaten and regarded almost as normal food. One of these is earth. An amazing number of people eat dirt. A habit which to most of us seems unreasonable and uncomfortable, but there are some quite good reasons for doing it.

Many mammals take in gravel and pebbles with their food, and these act as grinders in the stomach. Others need some sort of solid ballast or roughage as an aid to normal digestion. Wherever there is famine, earth is eaten as a food substitute to give a feeling of false repletion. It may also be taken for medical reasons. Certain clays in Sumatra are taken as a remedy for severe diarrhoea, while other clays on Java are prescribed as purgatives. The earth from termite mounds is a certain cure for all intestinal complaints in the Philippines, but in the Sudan it is considered to be more effective against syphilis. Pregnant women everywhere take to the soil to satisfy some random craving or in the explicit belief that it will avoid nausea, aid the delivery and make the child stronger. Earth may even be eaten to guard against good health. Black slaves in America ate large quantities of sand to make themselves too weak to work.

These are examples of occasional earth eating, but many people make no secret of their passion for soil and eat it all the time. In New Guinea they carry beads of clay on a string around their necks and, as they travel, pluck them off one by one to chew like gum. Local marl lime and soapstone are the favourite flavours. In Borneo salty mangrove mud is used as a spice. In Africa the soil is chosen with great care and that from particular areas is held in high repute. Vintage earths, often with salt and sugar added, are sold in the form of loaves in the markets of Mozambique.

Research shows that many of these soils do in fact contain minerals with medicinal properties. Earth eating, like many other apparently primitive food practices, turns out on examination to contain a sophisticated awareness of cause and effect. Eat this and so-and-so happens. It was not however until the Greeks tackled it that modern dietetics came into being. Hippocrates was the first to document the basic principles. He was followed in the first century BC by Celsus, who published an eight-volume guide to diet for sick people. Then came the mediaeval school, whose ideas were all based on folklore and hearsay. They carried the science through to the eighteenth century with such sparkling discoveries as 'hare's flesh doth engender melancholy' and 'beans are cold and hot in the first degree.'

In fact, very little progress was made until the early nineteenth century, when the chemical nature of food was taken into account for the first time. It was discovered that food was chemically broken down by digestion. In 1840, proteins, fats and carbohydrates were recognised as essential features of an adequate diet. By 1880 most food items had been correctly analysed, and the only major discovery – the identification of vitamins – had to wait until 1906.

Parallel with these later developments was a renewed interest in eating that flowered into the cult of the gourmet. Its discipline and ritual were first formalised by the French gastronomist Anthelme Brillat-Savarin. The performance of elaborate ceremonies over food and drink was based on simple physiology. Soup, for instance, was thought to stimulate the flow of digestive juices and was therefore placed at the beginning of the meal. Sweet tastes were correctly held to be less easily fatigued than the other tastes, so sweet dishes were relegated to the end of the meal.

These are only simple examples of a ritual which became increasingly complex and persists in many of its ramifications today. The details are familiar to anyone who has attended a formal banquet. Parts of the ritual have traditional origins and owe nothing to biology – there can be little significance in whether a decanter of claret is passed clockwise or counter-clockwise around a table. Biology only intrudes again at the end of the meal when the women leave the table to the all-male group of pseudo-hunters. The growth of the gourmet's ritual was designed to make the most of food and to foster the fellowship of those taking part in the meal. It is the nearest we in the 'civilised' West have ever come to the rites of hospitality practised by all 'primitive' communities.

Today human nutrition is a precise science. It has identified and classified all the substances in food and established the quantities of each necessary to maintain good health in various occupations and climates. It is now setting out to persuade people to eat the recommended diets – and is running into incredible difficulties.

We all vigorously defend our eating habits – what we eat is right and what others eat is wrong. We cling to the belief that reasonable food preferences determine our choice of food, while the other man's disgusting table manners are the result of food prejudices. The divergence in eating habits from race to race and from region to region within our species is unparalleled. Geographical and racial isolation have distorted the overall omnivority of the human species to produce all possible variations. There are now as many different kinds of food specialist in our one species as there are in the whole class of mammals. Since all of them survive, there is obviously no ideal diet for man. But most diets can be improved. The only way to begin any campaign for better eating is to understand what caused the divergence in the first place.

The most basic causal factor is geography. The climate and geology of each area dictate the type of food available there. At one extreme, there is only meat. The polar ice cap supports a community of species which are all carnivores – living off one another. In overpopulated tropical areas there is hardly any meat. And between the two is a complete spectrum of different types of omnivore. Every type has its own methods of coping with survival, and even in our comparatively uniform Western society, geographical variations manage to survive. Identical ingredients are used in widely different ways. From flour and beef alone come Lancashire hot pot, Cornish pasty, *cannelloni Napoletani* and American hamburgers.

After geography economics plays the most important role. A man's geographical situation determines whether his staple food is potato, rice, maize or yam. But his position on the economic ladder in that habitat determines what he eats with the staple. In all societies, the wealthier members eat more protein. The average amount eaten by the population as a whole is a good guide to the have and have-not societies. In Africa, the average meat consumption per person per day is forty grams, while in the Pacific it is more than 300. Each person in the Far East drinks about fifty grams of milk per day; in Europe the figure is nearer 500. These figures are useful guides, but they do not show who is actually getting the meat.

In most simple societies it is the chief or the elders who eat meat when it is available. And in many countries it is still the head of the household who is always given the most desirable foods like meat and eggs. In some countries, economics is linked to the social standing of the dish. In England today cockles and mussels are rather vulgar, while oysters are socially acceptable. A hundred years ago oysters were cheap and plentiful and eaten by everyone. Salmon also was common and farm labourers in the north went on strike because they were being fed too often on it. If oysters and salmon should ever be as popular again, they will rapidly fall from official favour. Status foods must be rare and expensive.

The part played in feeding by tradition is the most difficult to understand – and the most tenacious. In 1943 the rice crop failed in Bengal, and 3,000,000 people died because they refused to accept wheat as a substitute. Food habits, good and bad, are perpetuated and handed down like treasured family heirlooms from one generation to the next. Education has little or no effect. A recent survey of British mothers showed that they all believed brown bread to be better than white and sweets to be bad for the teeth. And yet ninety-two per cent of all bread sold is white, and the consumption of sweets in Britain is the highest in the world.

We eat what we like, and what father liked is good enough for us. Tradition dies very hard. The problem facing the nutritionists is that what people want is not necessarily what they need. And they are very reluctant to change. In Switzerland brown bread was subsidised in an attempt to promote sales, but without success. In Britain margarine still has to be coloured yellow to make it look like butter. In Puerto Rico free tomatoes and milk are scorned in favour of traditional beans and rice.

Even where food habits are changing, the change is not good. Already there is a growing number of cases of malnutrition in developing countries where preference is switching from the old foods to non-nutritious but very desirable sweets and soft drinks. It is not poverty that is causing the food-deficiency diseases in these areas, but a breakdown in the biological system brought about by artificial food. These have supernormal attractions that appeal very strongly to our rampant taste buds and lead to satisfaction of the psychological want for food without satisfying the physiological need. Once again man has developed too fast for his own good. We have developed a technology without the necessary safety devices and put ourselves at the mercy of manufacturers who are more interested in lining their pockets than our stomachs.

The game is going wrong. There are far too many casualties. We need to stop and rewrite some of the rules. Perhaps an instant playback will help put the problem in perspective. It goes like this:

Once upon a time there was a gatherer of food. He was one of a rare species, no more numerous than the great apes are today. He ate a very large number of things and, by virtue of his opportunism, ended up with a well-balanced diet. He thrived. But food getting took all his time, and, for an opportunist species, this was intolerable. He coveted the large food rewards he saw around him – the big game. So he worked out a way of getting them. His methods were so successful that he took to hunting intensively, but he never became a pure carnivore. Meat is rich in protein, but poor in variety – so he still supplemented his diet with odds and ends collected by his women. His numbers grew and some came to live in areas where large-grained grasses grew wild. He tried them and liked them. He gathered them and ground them and liked them even better. He took to living for longer periods where the grain and grapes grew best, and, eventually, he took to growing them himself.

He became a farmer and his life on the land was rich with starch and gradually poorer in protein. Domesticating wild animals restored the balance, but the returns were never as great. The settled life brought him companionship, food surpluses and specialists, but it deprived him of the high-protein diet he knew as a hunter. It also brought him many children, most of whom survived to have children of their own. Soon there were 20,000,000 and some of them produced no food at all – never setting foot on the land. They lived in towns and ate the farmer's food – and the bigger the towns, the farther the food had to travel. The farther it travelled, the better it had to keep – and the longest-lasting was plant food. By the time there were 100,000,000 of them, some had to go without meat altogether. Many more must go without today.

Good food means high protein food. This does not have to

be meat. Many vegetarians eat well-balanced meals without it. But it just so happens that meat is the most readily accessible source of protein, and those that cannot afford it can certainly not afford the vegetable alternatives. Meatlessness all too often goes with malnutrition. And malnutrition has a way of changing history. Wherever a large number of stomachs were empty enough to pool their hunger in a common cause, something happened.

The barbarian invasions of hungry Vandals and Visigoths broke up the Roman Empire. The Mongol conquests in Asia were entirely motivated by hunger and a shortage of grazing. In 1845 a shortage of potatoes in Ireland caused famine and sent enough people to the United States to effectively change the history of that country. Even in the last century it was still possible for hungry people to go somewhere else where there was more food. But what can happen today?

Every day there are more and more hungry people, and every day the communications between them are better and better. Nothing is more certain than that, sooner or later, a large number of them will try to move into some land of comparative plenty. All the lands with more food have fewer people, so their only defence lies in greater striking power – in nuclear weapons. They will have to use them. Then someone else is bound to retaliate, and in the end all that is left is contaminated food that no one can eat.

Our history has been shaped by the quality of the foods we ate. Our future is going to be determined far more by food quantity. There are now three billion of us and already two billion go hungry. Almost 500,000,000 are actually starving. But that does not stop them from breeding. Two babies are born every second, 172,000 every day, which is equivalent to adding the entire population of Great Britain to the world each year. People quoting these statistics usually talk in terms of living space. But all three billion living people can still be packed heel to toe into only 120 square miles. We could fit the world's total population into the Isle of Man or Malta or even Martha's Vineyard. So space is not yet a problem, but food definitely is.

We have all too easily assumed that man could go muddling

on and that bridges could be crossed as we came to them. But we have already reached a point where it is too late to avoid a major catastrophe. Population growth and food distribution have become so far out of step that the system is relentlessly heading towards its first complete breakdown. Even if all the resources of all the big nations were to be thrown now into a massive joint effort to produce and distribute more food, it would not arrive in time. Before the often-quoted deadline of 1984, hundreds of millions of human beings in Africa and Asia are going to die of starvation in a series of natural disasters that will make all the wars in history look like teething troubles. And there is *nothing* we can do about it. It is already too late.

All we can do is pick up the pieces afterwards and try to learn from our mistakes. The first lesson should be cooperation. There is enough food now to feed everyone alive, but too little is distributed and too much destroyed. Even with existing foods and our present, rather inefficient farming methods, we could feed about fifty billion mouths. We will have to do just this AD 2100 if the present rate of increase is maintained.

There is little at the moment to suggest that the birth rate will go down in the foreseeable future. So any plans we make must be based on the gloomy assumption that the population will continue to double every thirty-four years. Assuming that we reach the year 2100 without mishap, and have learned to cooperate well enough to distribute food evenly, we will be able to manage. But what happens after that?

One possibility is that we would have to eliminate all terrestrial wildlife and build roofs over all the cities and roads so that the entire land surface can be turned over to farming. This would enable us to support 100 billion. And if we all gave up eating meat and learned how to harvest the sea efficiently, we could just manage to feed 400 billion and make it to AD 2200. Then we would have to concentrate on the sea. The area of ice-free sea is about twice as large as the land, and all of it could be used to produce highly nutritious green algae. If all other life in the sea were eradicated, this would provide enough food for three million million people. There may be that many in 2300.

At this stage every person alive would have 150 square yards – about half the area of a tennis court. But even if two people with adjacent plots decided they would like to get together and play tennis, it would be impossible. No activity other than food production would be allowed. Every single spot exposed to the sun would have to be devoted to algae turning solar energy into food. More could be done if half the earth were not in darkness for half of each day. Continuous sunlight all over the world could be arranged by putting a number of enormous mirrors into orbit to light the whole globe all the time. This would bring the earth to tropical temperature, melt the ice caps, and allow us to support the twenty-five million million mouths that could need feeding by 2400.

And so it goes. There are several more tricks we could use to support even more people. But there is a natural limit. This is imposed by the heat generated by the people themselves. Even if we can feed them, the earth cannot remain cool enough to support life with more than one million million million people on board. If the population explosion goes unchecked, we could reach this absolute limit as soon as AD 3000. That is only a thousand years from now. If it sounds too far away to worry about, just remember that it is only as much time as has passed since the Norman conquest of England or Leif Ericson's discovery of America. And if the astronomic figures mean nothing to you, think of 120 people to the square yard. Today there are only .000006.

These predictions look on the blackest possible side. But, whatever happens, it is certain that food quantity will greatly concern us. We are on an evolutionary watershed between the Age of Quality and the Age of Quantity. Quantity can only be drastically improved at the expense of quality. The days of the gourmet are numbered. The supermarket syndrome will reach epidemic proportions as the markets themselves fall into the hands of big chemical combines which will be producing most of the food artificially.

Already they play a major part. Food distribution along the length of giant supermarket chains entails moving it for thousands of miles and keeping it in store for months. To make this possible, it has to be processed with preservative chemicals. Prefabricated heat-and-eat meals have to be specially synthesised and treated with sequestrant chemicals that keep fats and oils from becoming rancid. Emulsifying agents have to be added to make foods homogenise. Anticaking chemicals are added to salt, sugar and milk powder to keep them from clumping. And artificial colours and flavours have to be included in the formula to give the product some resemblance to the original food.

All these impurities are concealed behind obscure polysyllables like butylated hydroxyanisole and sorbitan monostearate in the small print on the back of the label. They masquerade as additives, suggesting that the consumer is getting something extra for his money rather than being deprived of the original flavour and food value.

At the moment, the manufacturers have to cater to man's demand for flavour and variety. It is easy enough to twist a chemical bond or prolong a reaction in a way which slightly changes the quality. But in time even this will become too expensive or take too long and will be abandoned in favour of greater profits and increased production. I can see absolutely no way in which we can continue to be omnivores enjoying fresh food qualities in an increasingly crowded world. Unless the population is stabilised at its present level, or even reduced, we will be forced into univority and perhaps even into oblivion.

The arguments against overpopulation usually cite the medical and social ill effects of crowding. But I believe that we can come to terms with these. I see the change in our eating habits as an even greater danger. Man can stay alive on nutritious mush, but he cannot stay sane. Food has so many non-nutritional values, feeding is such a vital social force, that I do not believe that we can survive without it. Given time, we could perhaps find a way – but we are not going to have time.

We are rushing headlong into something we do not understand. As a start, someone should set up a controlled experiment in which volunteers would be intravenously fed and forced to live in an environment where food and feeding do not exist. I predict that they would soon become completely disoriented and begin to show the same sort of psychological disturbances as subjects isolated in the dark or floating weightless in a tank of water.

And I suggest that we carefully consider the consequences before we condemn ourselves to an overcrowded existence and low-quality food. There is enough evidence in our present feeding behaviour to show that the science-fiction man who lives on occasional sips of nutrient solution is a good deal less than human.

We now know the basic rules of the game. But before we go on to play the next round, we should write a few rules of our own into the game. Rules which will ensure that everyone wins.

POSTSCRIPT

Most of the information in this book comes from my own research and experience. Part of it was gained in Africa and part in the Middle East, but three of my most formative years were spent in London. I am deeply grateful to the Zoological Society of London for providing me with generous research facilities during this time. And to Desmond Morris who guided me and whetted my appetite.

Where my work has been supplemented by that done by others, it has been mainly drawn from the following sources:

BATES, M, *Gluttons and Libertines*. Random House, New York, 1967.

BODENHEIMER, F. S, *Insects as Human Food*. The Hague, 1951.

BROTHWELL, D and P, *Food in Antiquity*. Thames & Hudson, London, 1969.

CLARK, W. E. LE GROS, *The Antecedents of Man*. Edinburgh University Press, 1959.

COLE, S, *The Neolithic Revolution*. British Museum, 1959.

FREMLIN, J. H, 'How Many People Can the World Support?' *New Scientist*, 24: 285 (1965).

GOODALL, J, 'Chimpanzees of the Gombe Stream Reserve,' in *Primate Behavior* (New York, 1965).

MORRIS, D, *The Naked Ape*. Cape, 1967.

——, *The Human Zoo*. (Cape, 1969).

OAKLEY, K. P, *Man the Tool-maker*. British Museum, 1961.

PIGGOTT, S, *The Dawn of Civilization*. Edinburgh University Press, 1965.

RENNER, H. D, *The Origin of Food Habits*. Faber & Faber, 1944.

RUSSELL, C and W. M. S, *Human Behaviour*. André Deutsch, 1961.
TINBERGEN, N., *The Study of Instinct*. Oxford University Press, 1951.
ZEUNER, F. E., *A History of Domesticated Animals*. Hutchinson, 1963.

LYALL WATSON

LIFETIDE

Continuing the process of questioning and exploration begun in his bestselling SUPERNATURE, Lyall Watson looks at recent developments in astronomy, biology and psychology, combining them with the experience of his own ten years' search into the mysterious.

A scientist himself, yet one who refuses to accept the traditional and self-imposed boundaries of science, he suggests that we are ourselves responsible for much that bemuses us, for phenomena such as ghosts, monsters and UFOs, for the supernatural and the extra-terrestrial.

In LIFETIDE, in the deep tidal flow of our unconscious, lie answers to the mysteries of dreams and visions, of precognition, reincarnation and human creativity itself.

'Mind-blowing, widely researched . . . richly rewarding, fertile, provocative, stimulating and exhilarating'
Graham Lord in the Sunday Express

'Lyall Watson has achieved a remarkable feat: he has managed to plait the diverse strands from his earlier books into a coherent philosophy – potentially a new biological paradigm'
Brian Inglis in The Guardian

sceptre

LYALL WATSON

THE BIOLOGY OF DEATH

'The only thing that makes death distinct from all other diseases and disorders is that everybody gets it'

Lyall Watson, bestselling author of SUPERNATURE, is convinced that it no longer makes *biological* sense to discriminate between life and death at any level. Here he presents an intriguing and original look at our ideas of and knowledge about that inescapable phenomenon.

Combining fifteen years of scientific research with his own theories and experiences, Dr Watson explores the very real problem of deciding when death actually occurs, and considers our psychological and social attitudes towards it. He discusses reincarnation, spiritualists and both other-body and out-of-body experiences, leaving little doubt that there is more to both life and death than we are able to comprehend by the evidence of our five senses . . .

'This is one of those books where a scientist, made fertile by his excitement about a subject, sparks off ideas in all directions, linking facts not before linked, trying out all kinds of associations'
Doris Lessing in The Guardian

'A brave, provocative and utterly fascinating book'
Sunday Express

LYALL WATSON

GIFTS OF UNKNOWN THINGS

Lyall Watson continues his fascinating investigation into so-called supernatural happenings which began with SUPER-NATURE. In his search for an understanding of other realities, Dr Watson became part of a small community living on a volcanic island in Indonesia, a community where extra-sensory perception, psychic healing, precognition, power places and survival after death are taken for granted . . .

In seeking explanations acceptable to the ever-changing theories of Western science, he describes an intriguing personal story which is a perfect blend of mystical happening and scientific investigation.

'It is, of course, completely different from the earlier books, but I found it equally absorbing. I found it one of the most fascinating things of its kind I have ever read'
Colin Wilson

'It is impossible not to be impressed and intrigued by his spectacular soundings in these strange waters'
The Observer

'It is his honest approach coupled with a willingness to encourage the reader to think things out for himself that makes his book a real contribution to thought'
Daily Telegraph

sceptre